SMOOTH CRIMINAL

_____

SMOOTH CRIMINAL

A One-Man American Crime Wave

Based on a true story

———————————————

BILL DEANE

PUBLISHED BY MUSE MEDIA LLC
in the U.S.A.
www.MuseMediaPublishing.com

*Based on a true story, although most persons names and some
locales and dates have been changed to protect the innocent.
For storytelling purposes, dialogue is by creation of the author.*

Deane, William T.
Smooth Criminal, A One-Man American Crime Wave;
William T. Deane aka Bill Deane—Second Edition.

Copyright © 2012 William T. Deane

Library of Congress catalog number:
1-804852981

Book designed and edited by Jennifer Deane

ISBN 978-0-9825112-4-4 (Mobi)
ISBN 978-0-9825112-7-5 (ePub)
ISBN 978-0-9825112-6-8 (Paperback)

DEDICATED to all those known and unknown who have suffered physically, mentally and financially under the clandestine prisoner-release program of the Federal Government.

WITH SPECIAL THANKS TO:
Bud Connell, Barbara Cronie, Liz Deane, Michael Hibblen, Mitch Lebe, Carol Magai, and Carl Muscarello and several others who unfortunately for their own safety cannot be thanked publicly. Without their help this book would not be possible.

Based on a true story, although most persons names and some locales and dates have been changed to protect the innocent. For storytelling purposes, dialogue is by creation of the author.

SMOOTH CRIMINAL

INTRODUCTION

I N THE FALL OF 1961, three guys in their 20s walked into a studio at the WFUN radio station, where Joey Green was a DJ, and shook his hand. The skinniest of the trio said "Hi, I'm Dave Riley but my stage name's Dee Thomas." He passed a disc in an envelope and said he wanted to be a rock 'n' roll star. There was nothing strange in that. Thousands of kids were trying to make it in the music industry. Getting air time on a major Miami radio station was a coup for any wannabe singer. While the other two, Leonard Owen and James Eaton, leaned against the wall, taking in the turntables and studio equipment, Dave said "It'd mean so much to me if you played my song."

He was no taller than 5'7" and wore a light-colored shirt and smart pants. His flattop was out of keeping with the current trend of letting the hair grow longer and greasing it into a quiff. It was the start of the swinging 60s. Roy Orbison, The Beach Boys, Ben E. King, Ray Charles and Motown had begun to propel America into a new era of music and free expression, but Dave Riley wasn't ready to say goodbye to the 50s just yet. He was a well-mannered, friendly guy, although not the type you might envision up on stage belting out rock 'n' roll like his life depended on it.

Music Director, Jim Timmons, had advised Joey that Dave and his friends would be stopping by. He said it was up to Joey. He didn't have to play Dee's track, but he could see on Jim's face that he'd be grateful if he did. Joey guessed that maybe he owed the guy a favor, but when he saw the label on the disc it was a real giveaway. The imprint in the middle told it was Mafia. Sometimes the Mob would invest in hopeful singers in the area.

Coincidentally, he'd seen a few boys in suits piling into Jim's office like they owned the place earlier that day. The Mob would often swing by to 'make friends' as it was referred to. The Mob viewed itself as an all-American business, so their men would feign humility, politely requesting you give their new singing sensation a whirl. It was one thing to turn down money or gifts from distributors, even if they were Mob owned and nobody ever gave you a hard time—but this was a different situation. The Mob was asking a favor of the station and if you weren't stupid, you said, yes.

The track went out on the airwaves a couple of days around 11PM to keep 'the boys' happy. It was an original version of a song written by Dee himself. Joey was being polite when he said it was mediocre, though he never had the heart to tell Dave, not even once, when they hung out a number of times, enjoying a few beers and spinning discs in his studio. Dave was epileptic and didn't have a license, so Joey sometimes drove him places in his new Corvette. Joey soon realized his first impressions were off-the-mark. The revolver in Dave's inside jacket pocket went with him everywhere. He'd run to the window, each time he heard a car door slam—pistol at the ready—like a character from a pulp fiction detective novel. Dave was jumpy, but Joey didn't ask questions.

In early 1962, Joey Green became a newsman at WGBS Radio and a weekend anchor at Channel 10, the ABC Miami television affiliate. On Friday, April 20th, he was getting ready to deliver the next WGBS newscast when he read a bulletin coming through on the UPI wire service about two guys who had skyjacked a Cessna from Tamiami Airport in order to fly to Cuba to join Fidel Castro's communist regime. Though the Cuba problem began during the Eisenhower era, worsening in the first days of Kennedy's tenure, it was the *Bay of Pigs* incident that forced everyone who followed the news, that a final showdown might suddenly occur. Tensions between the U.S. and its Southern neighbor had risen considerably over the past year.

The story said two young men had been arrested—David Riley and Leonard Owen. They had been dragged into a news conference at Miami International Airport, but they weren't allowed to talk. The Feds explained that Owen and Riley had hired a pilot, 23-year-old Reggie Doan, the week before for a sightseeing trip over Miami with the intention of kidnapping him at gunpoint to fly them to Cuba. Three Key West shrimpers were also on display at the news conference. The Feds arrested them for stealing a forty-thousand-dollar boat and sailing it to Cuba on the same day with the intention of defecting as well.

Joey felt his face flush as the realization hit him. "I know these guys!" he said aloud. Green thought back to the day when the trio walked into his studio, when Dee told Joey his real name was Dave Riley, and introduced his friends, both older, bigger and rougher-looking than their 22-year-old ring-leader.

The other newsmen, so busy going about their jobs, didn't take much notice of Joey's sudden outburst. Someone shrugged and said, "Oh yeah," but that was about it. Joey was the new guy on the bottom rung of the ladder.

After the *Bay of Pigs* fiasco, Cuban news was a daily occurrence not of much interest to non-Cuban Miami or the rest of the news guys at the station. But to Joey, this was a hot story.

Green read on. The three had been caught in Cuba, and bizarrely, Castro had sent Riley and Owen back to Miami International Airport on a Pan Am flight eight days later, along with the Key West shrimpers, where all five were immediately detained and charged. The story said that the men had been tortured and abused in El Principe prison in Havana, and Riley and Owen were now to be charged with kidnapping and air piracy which could earn them the electric chair.

It was insane to think that this guy was now a candidate for the death sentence. Riley and his buddies loved the Miami scene— lounging about on the beach, the pool parties, the hot girls. He didn't spout politics or come across as all that serious about anything. So, what was he doing in Cuba?

The kidnapped pilot, Reggie Doan, had also been returned to the U.S. by Castro and, having told the *Miami Herald* his story, the press was hailing him as a hero.

Being a hungry 22-year-old news junkie, keen to make his mark in the world, Green eagerly watched out for updates on the case. With Dave locked up, Joey had no idea he would ever see Dave again. He accepted his puzzling questions of why Dave hijacked a plane to Cuba probably would remain unanswered forever.

Then, out of the blue, in the early fall of 1962, Dee called the television station suggesting he and Joey meet at a Cuban restaurant on Tamiami Trail. Here Green was, out of curiosity, accepting an invitation for lunch with a felon the *Miami Herald* had been reporting was in jail awaiting trial. In the nearly empty restaurant, except for a single couple eating boiled fish and beans near a window, Joey took a seat opposite to Dave at 1:30PM.

Looking pleased with himself and swigging a bottle of beer on that hot afternoon, he said he was approached by an organization of some kind in jail when he was awaiting trail for an offense. He was released on the proviso he'd train to become an operative.

"But they sure didn't introduce themselves," Dave said. "And they didn't wear uniforms like the FBI, with big letters written across the back of their jackets. So I guessed they must be CIA."

His two buddies, Leonard and James had been brought on board for the missions at Dave's suggestion. On Friday, April the 13th, they had taken a single engine plane from Tamiami Airport on orders to fly to Cuba to spy. Their orders were to gather information and return to Miami, as they had successfully done many times before. Only this time was different. The Cuban Army caught them. While being interrogated, Eaton cracked and invented a phony story "to save his own skin," said Dave, sneering at the mention of Eaton's name, calling him a "squealer," exclaiming James' mouth could have easily killed him and Lenny.

Dave flashed a grin and leaned forward, elbows on the table, "You know what, Joey?—They spent two months turning me into being a Cuban. I looked like a Cuban, spoke like a Cuban and learned everything there is to know about Cuba. The CIA wanted me to blend in as a local citizen and infiltrate Castro's communist enclave, carrying out different assignments. Who would suspect a skinny 20-something in scuffed cowboy boots of being a spy?"

But the plan backfired and the Feds were feeling nervous about the court case and press questions. They had to cover up the fact that they had been carrying out spy operations abroad, particularly in a country where the U.S. had broken relations.

"What about this Reggie Doan guy?" Joey asked. "Where does he come into the story?"

"Ah him…" nodded Dave. "Reggie's a pilot at Tamiami Airport. He's made a few flights to Cuba for the Feds before, but he didn't fly this mission."

"Who did then?"

"James Eaton," Dave said. "But when he squealed, the Feds got scared and substituted him with Reggie Doan, so it'd look like just me and Lenny carried out the skyjacking, like the press is saying. Castro then shipped Lenny and me back on the flight, thinking we were just a couple of crazy kids on a joyride."

"And…" Green encouraged.

"The Feds covered their tracks by saying Lenny had been using the name James Eaton as an alias during the skyjacking and the press ate it up. As far as everyone is concerned, there never was a James Eaton on that flight, just Lenny using two names. Fucking clever, huh?"

"I guess…" Joey said with a puzzled look.

Dave wasn't finished, "But it nearly got screwed up. Eaton's name was used on the first news bulletin and then it was quickly changed to Reggie Doan as the pilot—and the press latched onto it. Lucky for the Feds, huh?"

"So, what did happen to James Eaton?" Joey asked.

"What do you think happens to squealers?" Dave took another

swig of his beer and laughed.

"This is too unbelievable…" Green said.

Dave's eyes were filled with excitement. "See that guy at the corner table?" Dave dipped his head raising his eyebrows.

Green saw a man in a dark business suit and tie, sitting alone. Coffee and a newspaper blocked his face. As Dave and Joey stopped talking, the man dropped the paper, folded it and stared at Green who stared back for a half-minute. The man then picked up the paper and without looking at them walked close by Joey and Dave's table. The serious-looking man then walked out the door without looking back.

"What was that all about Dave?"

"They have to know who I'm with at all times. He's a Fed— Joey, he's been following you for three weeks. If he suspects you'll go to the press about secret flights to Cuba and letting people like me out of jail, he could have you eliminated." Dave took another swig of beer and his grin widened.

Green couldn't believe what he was hearing. "Come on, Dave," he laughed nervously. "You're kidding me, right?"

"Nope! He's my driver, man. He's waiting for me outside in a government car."

Joey wasn't sure what to think at this point, but was glad to get out of there. He was just a young journalist back then and felt out of his depth. In later years, as a seasoned journalist, Green would have kept Dave there and questioned him all afternoon.

On the drive home, Green lost count of how many times he looked in his rear view mirror to see if he was being trailed. When he reached his apartment, relief coursed through his body. After their meeting at the Cuban Restuarant, he didn't see Dave for months and that suited him just fine. He didn't want to get embroiled in whatever it was Dave was up to.

IT WASN'T UNTIL YEARS later, after extensive research, that Green learned the full details of what became known as the *Black Friday Skyjacking* case. Green also uncovered the truth behind Dave's criminal career and lifetime involvement with the CIA. In the past, Green had switched between thinking Dave really could be mixed up with some shady deals and characters to suspecting that he was a fantasist. Dave had always wanted to be a superstar. He didn't hide that fact, but Joey was never sure what was truth or fiction as far as what Dave was telling.

In reality, David Thomas Riley became a dangerous felon, whose affable persona was a set-up, a manipulative and clever charade, which started long before he came into the radio studio in '61.

Riley's criminal career spanned five decades. He started out as a street punk, posing as a police officer attempting to extort money from an official for the Miami-Dade County planning division. He held up stores, ran a major drug operation, kidnapped and sexually assaulted a teenage girl, was a pimp, bigamist, gunrunner, thief and alleged murderer.

During his U.S. crime spree, he continued to carry out assignments for the CIA, and as he grew older his offenses grew in seriousness and scale. Now in his early 70s, he might be hidden somewhere under the government's Federal Witness Protection Program. Some of the victims of his crimes were too frightened to come forward, but others, though their names have been changed to protect their identities, were happy to share their stories.

ONE

———

WHEN DAVID THOMAS RILEY'S mother, Mary, gave the final push that thrust him into the world on June 2, 1939, the obstetrician in the labor room at Coral Gables Hospital, Miami, frantically scooped him up and placed him on heated towels on a medical trolley. He was a mottled purple color and his lips and fingernails were tinged blue with cyanosis. The child's limbs hung limply, like wrung out dish rags, as the doctor worked a miniature suction pump to clear the mucous from his blocked airways.

"Doctor, is the baby OK?" asked Mary, sitting up in her hospital bed.

The doctor played deaf. He wasn't going to tell her that her child was stillborn—not unless he had to. There was a chance they might be able to bring him around. It was a long shot but he was going to give it a good try.

As the doctor began gently pushing at the infant's tiny chest with two fingers he barked at the nurse.

"Temperature?"

"32 degrees centigrade, doctor," she replied.

"OK, not good. Not good at all," He mumbled and carried on with the chest compressions. He pushed a couple more times in quick succession and then stopped.

"What's going on?" Mary wailed petrified at the sight of the medical staff rushing backwards and forwards. She tried to get a glimpse of her child, but there were too many people blocking her view.

"Someone, see to the mother," ordered the doctor over his shoulder and then focused on the infant again. "Come on...come on..." he said under his breath, only being heard by the two nurses either side of him. He lightly pumped at the baby's chest and was still for a moment. "Good. Great. He's breathing! We need to get him to the stabilization room, quick!"

Mary had given birth to four other sons and she knew the drill. There were no baby cries to fill the air this time and it was clear that there was something gravely wrong. But no one was paying any attention to her volley of questions. When she realized that she was not going to be handed her child for his first cuddle, her anxiety grew. Even when she stretched her arms out, the medical team ignored her, too busy hooking up apparatus, clear tubing and machinery. She began to cry and tried to clamber down off the bed in her hospital gown. Before her bare feet hit the linoleum a nurse came rushing over and tried to coax her back into bed.

"Mrs.. Riley..." she began.

"What's wrong with my baby, doctor?" Mary asked again. Sweat caked her brown bangs to her forehead and her fingers shook in front of her mouth as she spoke. "I want to see my child! Please!"

Exhausted from a 14 hour labor, the nurse managed to gently

push the patient back into a horizontal position. "Please try and stay calm Mrs. Riley," she said.

"Don't worry Mrs. Riley, we're doing everything we can for him," chimed in the doctor, who placed the child on a trolley and made sure that his oxygen mask was firmly in place before he was to be transferred to another part of the hospital for close monitoring.

Mary thought she had heard straight but she wasn't sure. She frowned. "He? It's a boy?"

"Yes, it's a boy," answered the nurse, still with her hand on the patient's shoulder.

Mary ignored the nurse's gesture and sat bolt upright again. "What's wrong? Where are you taking him? Why isn't he crying? Where's my husband? I want my husband!"

While his mother sobbed, a very unwell David was wheeled out of the labor room by the doctor, with the rest of the team close behind. He had clung onto life by a miniscule thread.

"Please try and calm down," soothed the young nurse. "Your husband's outside, waiting in the corridor. I'll go get him."

"My son…"

"He's being taken to intensive care now, Mrs. Riley. Try and calm down," she repeated and then followed briskly after the others.

"But I want to see my baby!" shrieked Mary. Patrick Riley came rushing into the room and put his arms around his distraught wife. But even her husband's presence couldn't console her. Mary didn't care about anyone else. She only wanted to feel her child nestling in her arms, like any new mother.

"It's not fair!" she cried.

A week after David's unhappy entrance into the world, Mary and Patrick walked out of Coral Gables Hospital with David wrapped snugly in a baby blanket.

"I never thought we'd get to see this day," said Mary.

"Let's go home, honey," nodded Patrick with his arm draped over his wife's shoulders. "See the boys."

The summer sun shone down on the threesome reflecting off of the wide white building behind them. Palm trees swayed in the breeze. It would have made the perfect photograph. Their son had nearly died, but their prayers had been answered. To the nurses, her husband and anyone else who would listen, Mary expressed gratitude over the miracle that saved their baby. They were good Catholics and they had been truly blessed.

Still small and weak, baby David was out of the woods and the doctors felt confident enough to discharge him. Baby David was about to meet his four big brothers, who had been looked after by their paternal grandmother.

Although set in affluent Coral Gables, the Riley house was a modest three-bedroom place, which survived the Labor Day hurricane of 1935, four years before David's birth. Many houses on the street were blown away, so all new buildings were constructed out of heavy cement blocks. Close to 900 were killed in that Labor Day hurricane, but luckily, Dave's family survived the trauma and their home was saved with some major repairs.

Patrick Riley was a lawyer and had been doing okay in the thirties' depression. Mary prided herself on being a good mother and housewife. Patrick junior was nine, his brother Sean was seven, Brian four and Dolan, three. They were healthy, sturdy boys and liked to rough house with their father, wrestling on the living room floor or throwing a ball about in the yard. They were a typical middle-class family in what many considered the most attractive Miami suburb.

The community was a fairly close-knit one. The younger kids in the area would spend summer months congregating on the beach at Coconut Grove, collecting land crabs after dark. And on Saturdays, it was 15 cents a pop to see a matinee for anyone under 16. Before TV came in the late 40s and early 50s, entertainment came to movie theaters, palatial buildings with life-sized marble statues and cascading water fountains in the lobbies.

Judy Garland's *Over the Rainbow* and big band swing tunes of Glenn Miller, Tommy Dorsey and Benny Goodman jazz bands, were everywhere as America quickly merged from the ten-year depression right into a war. The Great Depression of the 30s was on its last legs and things were looking up again. Attorney Patrick Riley, exempt from the draft with a family of five children, felt Coral Gables becoming a place of regeneration and optimism and Dave's birth added to his sense of hope.

Mary Riley was a homebody, happy to spend her days with her family, baking or mulling around in the garden. Patrick and her four older sons were a tight group, but Dave spent most of his time as a little boy with his mother and liked to follow her around as she went about her chores. Mary adored her youngest son and knowing he was more vulnerable than the others, protected and encouraged him.

It was around age three that he had his first fit, arms and legs flailing on the kitchen floor, his brothers watching on in horror from the breakfast table. Dave was diagnosed with epilepsy and was given drugs to keep the condition under control. From then on, Mary kept an even closer eye on Dave and the gulf between him and the rest of the males in the family grew wider. They saw him as being different. He even looked different, with his floppy brown hair, pale skin and whip-thin limbs. Patrick, Sean, Brian and Dolan were outdoorsy, active kids and their time on the baseball and football fields showed in their broadening physiques. Whereas Dave had no interest or talent for sports and his ill health meant he was prone to picking up colds, the flu, and other infections going around.

His brothers never invited him to join in with their games and if Mary asked them to take Dave to the park to play baseball, the boys would complain, "Ah, but Mom, he can't even hit a ball!" or "Can't we leave him here? He's a drag!"

If being epileptic wasn't bad enough, Dave was also dyslexic. While the other kids in fifth grade could write short stories and read aloud in front of the class, Dave stumbled over his words, causing the other children to call him a "dummy." Dave would spend lunchtime sitting cross-legged on the grass, watching everyone else running about, enjoying themselves. Resenting being ill and different, he decided on his own he didn't need his pills. He began to lie.

"David, are you sure you took your pills?" Mary would ask, before he headed to school.

"Yes, Mom."

"You know what'll happen if you forget." She stooped down to look him in the eye. "You don't want to get ill again, sweetie."

"Yes, Mom. I took them."

Although Mary always called him "special," Dave just wanted to be the same as other kids his age. However, his condition worsened and soon he was having frequent fits during lessons.

"Give him some room!" yelled the teacher, when he fell from his chair, crashing to the floor. The other children huddled around to watch as his arms and legs jolted and spittle leaked from the corner of his mouth. "Back to your desks!" the teacher ordered Dave's classmates.

"What's wrong with him?" asked a girl.

"He's a retard," said another.

"Back to your desks at once!" the teacher repeated.

Much to Dave's humiliation he came around as he was being stretchered into an ambulance, with the whole school watching. When his parents found out he hadn't been taking his medication his mother cried with frustration and young Dave could sense his father's disappointment.

Dave was immediately hooked when he first heard Frank Sinatra sing. He spent a lot of time in bed, listening to music on the radio. It was his escape machine taking him away from his social problems. He practiced singing in the bathroom—toothbrush mimicking a microphone. Dave was determined that one day he would be a star, envisioning he'd get his father front row seats at his first Vegas show while turning his brothers away if they asked him for tickets. One day they would regret ignoring him. Music became his obsession and that stayed with him thoughout his life.

Dave's fantasy world grew in proportion as he hit his teens and served as a buffer against the solitary reality of his home life. He soon began to make up stories about his accomplishments at school, his abilities and how popular he was.

"I hit a home run! The teacher wants me for the team!" said Dave one day at 13 years of age.

"Yeah right," sighed Brian, by now a strapping 17. "Hey Dad, let's go watch a game this weekend!"

"Sure, Brian," replied Patrick senior from behind his newspaper. "That's a great idea."

"That's nice, David dear." Mary leaned over and smoothed his hair. "You'll be a great asset to the team."

"Thanks, Mom," while looking at his father.

His brothers didn't like David being around. They did their own thing and David did his. They learned to tell when he was telling the truth or lying, but didn't care.

As he got further into his teen years, he began to think about ways of bringing attention to himself, the role of anti-hero, the outcast, misunderstood genius. Through his deeply entrenched resentment simmered the beginnings of rebellion.

Dave began coming home in the early hours and sleeping until the afternoon when he would head out again. No one in the family had any idea what he was doing when away from the house. He often asked his mom for money, which she readily gave him.

"Stop treating David like a baby, Mary," Patrick Sr. snapped at her. "You've always spoiled him. He should get off his backside and get a job, like his brothers!"

The day came when Dave crammed his belongings in one suitcase and muttered "goodbye." Only his mother asked where he was going before he slammed the front door behind him. Patrick thought some independence would knock some sense into his youngest son. He had always lectured his boys to work hard and aim high.

"Maybe it'll turn him around, Mary," he soothed.

"But he's such a sensitive boy," she said, tears brimming. "And now he's out there all alone."

Patrick's eyes rolled to heaven. "He needs to toughen up," he sighed. "He can't rely on his mommy all his life. He needs to get an education and find his own way."

While actually brilliant, Dave had no intention of going to college like his siblings. Why bother, he thought. He was already smart and had talent.

By 20, he was ready to make his dream a reality. It was 1959 and Bobby Darin had hit the number one spot with *Mack the Knife* and that was Dave's kind of song.

Dave planned to be a singing star too, but first he needed to make some money and he wasn't about to shovel fries in a crummy burger joint to get it. He was better than that and was determined to show the world what he was made of. Dave Riley would not be ignored any longer.

TWO

THREE YOUNG MEN SAT in a nine-year-old Ford Custom convertible parked outside Coral Gables bus station on Salzedo Street listening to the radio. Keeping time with the beat, Dave Riley tapped his finger on the butt of his 32 caliber revolver, which was wedged in a leather chest holder under his cheap sports jacket. He had taken his shirts home to his mom to be washed and ironed a few days before and he had picked out a striped blue one for this occasion. He liked to feel the starched crispness of the cotton against his skin. His beige pants were also freshly pressed. Any other respectable street punk just weeks past his 21st birthday would normally only be caught out in public sporting a battered biker jacket and greased up hair, but Dave wasn't one to follow the pack. He didn't go in for the whole freestyle mumbling Brando thing that other hustlers his age had adopted. He was his own man and in his mind he was on important business. He had it all mapped out.

"Man, what time is it?" asked Leonard Owen, Dave's best buddy, from the driver's seat. A solid-built guy, five years older than his pal, often drove Dave around being he was unable to get behind the wheel due to his epilepsy and refusing to take his medicine. Riding shotgun was James Eaton.

Leonard Owen was Dave's right hand man and James Eaton was happy to hang around with them both, hoping that some easy money might find its way into his pockets. Dave provided the two men with a buzz of excitement that took them away from their days of being bums, hanging around on street corners or doing dead-end jobs like pumping gas or selling shoplifted booze and cigarettes. Lenny and James went way back, having met up in a local park many times while Dave was skipping class. Both about five years older than Riley, had first bumped into him in a late-night drinking den, where the Miami street punks or wannabe gangsters hung out. But Dave was different. He was no gum-chewing wonder with a sneer denting his top lip. Dave had class, even at 16, his new friends observed. Lenny and James were sucked in by his talk of being in with top record producers and the crème de la crème of the Miami Mob. They thought Dave was connected, that he was heading somewhere and wherever this kid was going they decided they wanted to get there with him. Lenny in particular was in need of someone to believe in, to look up to.

Dave sighed and looked at his watch. "7:30. How many more times you gonna ask me that?"

His other friend, James, leaned in from the back and addressed Dave in the passenger seat. "Where is he? I can't see him."

"He'll be here," said Dave. "You got the pictures?"

James handed Dave a brown envelope. Riley tugged out a bunch of 8x10 black & white photos, smiled and pushed them back in the envelope. "You caught him at a really good angle there, Lenny."

"Yeah, Dave, I just love taking photos of naked men." Leonard screwed his face up and shuddered.

"I sure as hell wouldn't want those getting in the wrong hands if I were him," said Dave. "He better have the money."

It was a warm evening on Monday June 27, 1960, and people were entering and exiting the front doors of the little bus station with the capacity to hold six buses underneath an outdoor roof so those waiting could be protected from Miami's typical ten-minute summer rainstorms.

During the previous week, the Mob had passed Dave the name and description of the mark he was now waiting to meet at the bus station. During his briefing in the office of a local record label run by a guy named Tony, Riley had been told that financially-set Raymond Hooper, mid-40s was a highly respected intellectual from a Catholic family, an expert in architecture and urban design who worked for the county planning division. He had been sleeping with a 19-year-old waiter named Adam. In the early 60s, it was an outrage to be openly gay in the U.S. and the Mob knew that the scandal would ruin Hooper professionally and socially if he was outed. He made an ideal target. The details had been passed through Tony to Dave by one of the Mafia bosses who had no doubt been given the orders by someone else even further up the hierarchy.

It was Dave's first shakedown for 'the boys' and he was eager to impress, to show that he was no slouch. The Mafia ran or had some hold over the smaller record labels in the area and through his inquiries about cutting a record, Dave had at once been welcomed into 'the family' like a long lost son. He was touched and honored that the 'big boys,' the top rung of the local Mafioso no less, wanted him on board. They knew how to sniff out a money-hungry kid with street smarts and he was a prime candidate for carrying out the lucrative practice of extortion.

Riley knew that if he did a good job on this night Tony and his bosses were going to help him make it in the music business, and with their connections, he was sure to be the next Frank Sinatra. He could feel it in his bones, he was on a one way ticket to super stardom. The wannabe, pictured his brother Brian knocking on his dressing-room door holding his hand out for money and then he slamming the door square in his face.

Leonard Owen and James Eaton were brought on board for the scam and the three of them had been sent to photograph Raymond Hooper in a compromising position in order to later blackmail him. The three had waited outside Adam's place in the Coconut Grove area ready to capture both him and Hooper on film.

WHEN JOEY MET DAVE in the Cuban restaurant on Tamiami Trail two years later, after his arrest for the skyjacking, Dave laughed and slapped the table with the flat of his hand while he recalled the night outside Adam's apartment building. Riley wasn't shy about talking about his various escapades and as extortion was his first foray into full-time crime, he was even keener to spill.

"Joey, get this. The three of us climbed up the fire escape at the back of Adam's apartment building in the dark. Me and James hitched Lenny up by his legs while he pointed the camera through the open bathroom window next to the bedroom. But Lenny nearly dropped the camera in the wash basin under the window, the big idiot. Then Lenny saw the two of them and took the shots. Let's just say they weren't playing cards in there if you know what I mean. Not something I ever want to see again, two faggots going at it like stars in a porno flick." He pulled a face. "Still gives me nightmares."

"What did you do with the pictures?" Joey asked.

"What d'you think?" Dave took a swig of beer and put the bottle back down.

"I trailed Hooper for a few days, waited for him in the parking lot of his building. I pulled my pistol, pressed it under his jaw and told him I was a cop, flashed him some fake ID, showed him the pictures and said I had plenty of copies. I thought he was gonna cry."

"Did he pay you off?"

"I told him he better get me $5000 or everyone would know about his extra curricular activities."

"What did he do?"

His voice was calm and low. "I was up real close, you know. I had the pistol shoved right in Hooper's face like this." Dave held an invisible weapon to his head, doing all the actions. "He begged me not to shoot him and said he needed time to get his hands on that kind of money."

Green motioned for him to carry on.

"I said he had till Monday to get me the money. If he didn't turn up at the Gables bus station at 7:30PM, the pictures would go public. I thought he was gonna wet his pants."

"Did he turn up?"

"Yeah, but he was a few minutes late."

DAVE STILL HAD HIS index finger on the butt of his revolver
while he sat in Lenny's car and scanned the bus station doors,
watching people passby on their way home. He saw groups of
kids hanging about, waiting for friends from the poorer northwest
section of the city so they could head downtown.

"Man, what time is it?" asked Lenny.

"Shut the fuck up," snapped Dave, as he spotted Hooper among
the crowd.

The slim middle-aged guy slipped into the little building; neat
navy jacket, glasses, nondescript face, thinning hair combed over
to hide a small bald area. Dave told his two sidekicks to wait by
the entrance of the station and to look out for cops. He got out of
Lenny's car and with his hand still on the revolver hidden only by
his jacket, he strolled into the bus station and stood to one side of
the entrance, watching, while Hooper was rooted there, glancing
nervously around him. Dave leaned against the wall scanning the
area. One sniff of a damn cop and he was out of there, but it was
clear. He then clocked his target's shiny slip-on shoes, the spotted
tie and shook his head, thinking what a total nerd this Hooper guy
was. He had also noted that he was carrying a package, wrapped in
brown paper, the kind people put sandwiches in. Dave sauntered
confidently towards him, both hands sunk in trouser pockets, jacket
collar flipped up, knowing the $5000 was just moments away from
being his and how impressed the Mob was going to be. He stopped
and tapped Hooper on the arm. The guy swung around. Dave could
see that he was terrified and already sweating. Hooper's eyes were
bloodshot behind his gold-rimmed glasses and Dave wondered if
he'd been crying.

"It's…it's you," Hooper said looking furtively around him.

"Who were you expecting? Frank Sinatra?" Dave replied and took a step closer to Hooper, who backed away a few paces. He glimpsed a flash of the pistol wedged in Riley's chest holder and gulped, praying that he wasn't about to do something reckless like use it. Hooper didn't want to die in a bus station or anywhere else. He had seen enough movies. One wrong word or quick move could take a punk like this by surprise and it could be a case of shoot first, think later.

Dave Riley, on the other hand, hadn't been doing a lot of clear thinking around that time. He hadn't bargained on who he termed a 'white-collar, middle-class wimp' like Hooper going to the authorities to report him just two nights earlier. Raymond Hooper's sense of justice had taken firm hold after Riley left Hooper shaking in his shiny shoes in the car lot of his own municipal building. Hooper had seen the fake police badge, the pictures of him cavorting with his young lover and felt a pistol at his jaw. Raymond Hooper went directly from that dark car lot to the Florida Assistant State Attorney Arthur Hunter's office to report the crime that had unfolded just a half-hour before.

Raymond Hooper was a much braver man than Dave gave him credit. Hooper felt the risk of being outed as a practicing homosexual, fired from his job and maybe killed while caught in the middle of crossfire in a public bus station, was preferable to being blackmailed. He knew that if he paid up once, it was likely the perpetrator would come back for more money. He refused to live like that. In fear of his secret getting out and his upstanding reputation being left in tatters, Raymond Hooper did his civic duty and blurted out the whole sorry saga from start to finish to Arthur Hunter and his men. The police then assured an almost hysterical

Hooper that they would keep the real story from the press if he promised that he would turn up at the bus station as pre-arranged and meet Riley. After assuring Hooper a dozen times or more that detectives would be in hiding, waiting and watching his back, he agreed to the plan. A trap was set.

Hooper was trembling much harder now, even his fingers fluttered at his sides. It pleased Riley that he had such a strong effect on a grown man. Obviously, Hooper hadn't been around dangerous people like him before. No wonder the poor schmuck was in such a state. You couldn't blame the guy for that, Dave conceded.

Riley leaned forward and gestured toward the package, which sent Hooper into panic overdrive. He stumbled back a few paces and with his eyes in the direction of the pistol stuttered, "Sorry I'm late…the traffic was awful so I had to take…"

Dave cut him off, wanting to grab the cash and get out of there. "Look, I'm not here for a fucking traffic report, buddy. I'm a busy man. That's the money, huh?" Dave's chin dipped in the direction of the paper bag.

"Umm…" Hooper tried to appear calm as his head swiveled to the side slightly to see if he could spot the two Miami Dade County plain clothes police officers who he thought had been down by the station's newsstand earlier, but there was no one there. Hooper's eyes flicked to the right of the ticket office and saw who he hoped might be a cop in a suede jacket, but he couldn't be sure. He took a breath, then another. He had to stay in control. He knew guys like this could kick off at any given moment. They were loose cannons. Maybe he was the kind of criminal that didn't care if he lived or died and there was going to be a hail of bullets with Hooper caught in the middle. It didn't bear thinking about.

A big muscular guy with red hair and dark blue jeans was in front of the ticket counter to his left, just standing still. Hooper's eyes glided eastwards once and rested back on Dave, who was now fidgeting and restless. Riley checked that no one was looking at him, opened his jacket a little and flashed Hooper the pistol.

"Is that the $5000?" he whispered, motioning towards the bag. "I told you, I'm a busy man."

"Yes," said Hooper, his face and shirt collar drenched in sweat. He held the package out towards Dave with a shaking hand. "Take it. Look, I just want to go home."

Dave snatched the bag and said impatiently, "It had better all be there or you'll be fucking sorry."

Just as he had it in his grasp Dave felt someone grab his elbow and say, "I think I should inform you that you're under arrest for attempted extortion."

"What the fuck…?" Dave looked from Hooper to the huge red-haired guy built like an airplane hangar to his right, who gave him a brief flash of his police badge. By his side were five other smirking police officers in plain clothes. The big red-haired cop took the bag of money off Dave while he tried to wrench his arm out of the man's grasp.

"Hey, what're you doing?" he stammered, forcing a cheesy smile that didn't seem to reach as far as his eyes this time. "There's been some kind of mistake here, guys. I'm a Metro police officer too."

"Oh really?" said one of the cops.

"Yeah, really, I am," Dave nodded.

"Yeah and I'm Bo Diddley," said the red-haired officer, seizing

Dave's wrists and slapping hand cuffs on him. The other officers sniggered at their colleague's impressive wit.

"It's true! I'm a cop!" Dave carried on as two more men grabbed him and pushed him towards the bus station exit.

A small crowd of scruffy teenagers had gathered and was having a ball watching the action. Dave weakly struggled against the officers, trying to yank his arms out of their grasp. "Hey, come on now, guys. What's with the cuffs? I'm a cop!"

"No, we're cops, dumb-ass," said the arresting officer, shaking his head as he caught the eyes of his two colleagues holding onto Riley. He sighed heavily and in a bored voice repeated the words he'd said many times before, "You have the right to remain silent. You have the right to an attorney…"

By this point Dave knew there was no use in carrying on with the lie. But he wasn't done.

"OK, you got me there, I admit that," he floundered. "But I'm a respectable guy…a businessman…I'm the vice president of a local record company…"

"Yeah, yeah, yeah," cut in the red-haired cop and opened the back door of his parked unmarked squad car. Dave, escorted to the police station and was booked, still maintaining he was a big cheese in the music business and could get them free Sinatra tickets.

When the local press got hold of the story Dave may not have gotten his name in lights like he always dreamed, but seeing it in print gave him his first taste of fame or ill-fame. There was no private dressing room, with a crowd of admirers waiting for a grand stage entrance—only an eight-by-six concrete cell at Miami Dade County Jail.

THREE

TWO MORNINGS AFTER DAVE'S arrest *The Miami Herald* ran the headline, "Man Faces Extortion Charges." The article, buried on page six of the newspaper read, "A 21-year-old Coral Gables man attempted to shakedown a county employee for $500, police said Tuesday." As agreed with Raymond Hooper prior to the set-up and arrest of Riley at the bus station, State Assistant Attorney, Arthur Hunter, and the Miami Dade Police had come up with a cover story minimizing the extortion and the press and public bought it. Hooper's secret was safe.

The Mob was never into petty crime. There was no way they would have gotten out of bed for a crumpled brown paper package holding $500. They had done their background research and were fully aware that Raymond Hooper was high up in the city's planning department, had a plush apartment a stone's throw from the beach and wasn't short of a few bucks. Plus the clincher, the Mob knew how much Hooper had to lose if caught with his pants down, so to speak. There was no mention either of the photographs of Raymond Hooper and Adam caught in flagrante delicto in the article and the whole crime was left as vague as possible for the press. The *Miami Herald* piece went on to say that David T. Riley, of Obispo Avenue, posed as a Metro police officer, threatened to have Hooper arrested "on a trumped up charge" and was accused of accepting "marked money in a blackmail payoff." Hooper's gamble in going to the authorities had paid off. His job and his reputation were still in tact and Dave Riley was languishing in a crummy cell in a light green prison issue jumpsuit in Miami Dade County Jail.

It was easy to understand why Dave's brothers grew to not believe a word he said when he was a teenager. However, when the press came knocking at their father's door looking for infomation on their little brother after the bus station incident, they soon sat up and took notice. But, as the family found out what Dave actually did with his time, and that he was indeed up to no good, they reverted back to pretending he didn't exist.

Riley found himself spending most of the summer of 1960 in a prison cell in Miami Dade County Jail for the extortion attempt against Hooper awaiting trial, along with his two best friends. James Eaton and Leonard Owen had also been arrested for attempting to drive away from the outside of the bus station the night of the shakedown.

Dave had told them to watch out for cops, but being the officers were in plain clothes, they hadn't been able to warn Dave and had then tried to make a getaway when they saw Dave being cuffed by whom they assumed was a big red-haired detective. Eaton and Owen hadn't noticed the other non-uniformed cops outside the bus station watching them while they leaned on the hood of Lenny's car waiting for Riley. When the two jumped into the car, it was too late. They were cornered by officers on foot and a squad car at the exit. Although they denied any involvement in the attempted extortion, they were now sharing cells with some of the less salubrious street hustlers the jail housed. Lenny, physically big and almost as bigheaded as Dave, could stomach prison life, but James, being picky about with whom he socialized, was none too happy to be squashed into a cell with whom he labeled "stinking low life." The three saw themselves as a cut above your common garden thief, pimp or drug dealer, even in the early days of their blossoming felonious careers.

"Man, they stuck me in the bottom bunk with some stinking fat pig above my head," James moaned to Dave and Lenny as they spooned grey porridge from plastic trays one morning in the prison cafeteria. The large room was filling up with prisoners, making their way towards the food counter or tables that were lined up in neat rows. "At night the creep keeps me awake snoring, farting or jacking off." Dave and Lenny burst out laughing at their friend's disgusted face. "It ain't fucking funny, guys. I haven't had any sleep in a week."

"Stop bitching, will you, James? We'll be out of here soon." Dave said.

"How d'you know?" asked James.

Dave glanced around him and motioned for his two friends to lean in closer. "I had a visit from the Feds yesterday afternoon."

"Huh? What're you talking about?" Lenny's broad face was confused.

"What d'you mean, the Feds?" asked James, sliding his tray of slop away from him like it was contaminated with some tropical disease.

"Look, they didn't wear suits with FBI written across them or anything like that, but they were Feds. I reckon most probably CIA. They gave me an IQ test. I scored high—150." Dave looked to his friends, waiting for an impressed reaction, but got nothing. "They said they could get me out of here," he whispered while other men in prison jumpsuits chatted and shouted around him.

The CIA never announced itself, and having evolved from other World War II agencies, the public was unsure whether it was actually the agency behind the 'Take-Down-Castro-Operation' in Cuba. Since the early 70s, nothing could be more certain the Firm was the brains behind the failed operation to rid Cuba of Castro and communism. Dave had guessed right. It was the CIA

"You getting out? Lucky for some then, huh, Dave?" Lenny sulked.

"I'm going to see if I can swing it so you two come too. They need smart guys like us."

"Really?" Lenny looked happier.

"That's understandable enough," shrugged James.

"So what do they want guys like us for, huh, Dave?" asked Lenny.

"They need spies for secret missions to Cuba and stuff," Dave replied.

James snorted, his green eyes rolling upward. "Man, you been smoking weed again?"

"I'm not joking, James. I told them you can fly a plane."

Like many people in Florida, James held a license to fly a Cessna. He had been obsessed with flying since he was a kid and as soon as he had enough spare cash he invested in lessons at the age of 21.

James grinned. "You did? What did they say?"

"Not much. Just that it could be useful."

"Hey, what about me?" Lenny was worried.

"You're my right-hand man, Lenny. Like always."

"What a great plan, Dave!" said a smiling Lenny.

"Let's hope they don't need you two to take IQ tests as well though," frowned Dave.

"Why?" asked Lenny.

"There's no way they'll let you in then," laughed Dave.

"Very funny, man." James' eyeballs rolled upwards again.

"Just stick with me, guys," said Dave, sitting back in his plastic chair. "There isn't going to be any trial. We're out of this shithole."

"Really, Dave?" asked Lenny, for reassurance.

"Hey, have I ever let you down?"

"Nope," Lenny shook his head.

"They practically begged me to work for them," Dave smirked. "I think they wanted me to go with them then and there, like that." Clicking his thumb and middle finger together, "I told the them—I said—'Hey, I don't go anywhere without my boys around me.'"

SMART, PATRIOTIC AMERICANS FROM prestigious colleges and universities made an attractive match for employment with the Central Intelligence Agency. The pursuit of the American dream having its foundations firmly set in the ethics of hard work, justice and freedom for all, didn't hurt either. As the Agency got more deeply involved in complicated, clandestine operations, brilliant and dedicated agents looked for assistance from operatives, willing to gamble their life in exchange for freedom from a prison cell. Only a tiny percentage of the jail population fit the Agency's requirements, but they numbered more than enough for their needs. The candidates had to be street-smart, confident to the point of being cocky, certain, if questioned, they'd be able to talk themselves out of any situation, as well as willing and able to succeed at the intensive operative training before being assigned to covert operations in such places as Japan, Taiwan, Vietnam, Thailand, Philippines, eastern Europe and of course, Cuba.

Although never overtly political, Dave loved his country to a fervent passion and wanted to fight Castro's regime, but Dave also yearned for the kudos he envisioned being a spy would bring. The CIA admired his spunk, but the work was too secretive for public thanks to the hired guns. Operatives carried no authority and gained little respect from their bosses who sent them on dangerous missions to foreign countries, sometimes never to return.

The Agency answers only to the President and to Congressional oversight commitees, raising the question, does the Agency tell all to whom it is responsible? In the 1950s and early 1960s, the CIA's leaders, such as Allen Dulles and John McCone were great advocates of covert missions within coups, foreign labor unions, anti-Communist insurgencies, political parties, and setting up and running publishing houses, shipping companies and other organizations, all of which required considerable man power. After the *Bay of Pigs* fiasco in April 1961, covert action and missions became much riskier politically and the Agency found itself in hot water on several occasions. Press revelations and major news stories during the 1960s, reporting CIA maneuvers of questionable legality, including the *Bay of Pigs* fiasco, plus congressional investigations, helped to negatively impact the

Agency's reputation. By the time the 70s dawned, working for the CIA no longer held the same prestige and people began asking some seriously embarrassing questions, especially when ex-CIA agents and case workers turned to publishing books worldwide, lifting the lid on the dealings of what was once was a top secret revered agency.

COCKY AND SMART PRISIONERS were a perfect fit for the CIA operation. They didn't need sensitive personalities or individuals who struggled with a strong sense of conscience and asked questions. More than anything, new operatives had to be pliable and loyal. Dave Riley was all these things and had little empathy with others.

"How badly do you want to get out of jail? Willing to risk your life for your country? The pay will be great. Your freedom between assignments will be complete, " said the Agent. "In or out?"

"In," Dave readily declared.

During the summer of 1960, Dave Riley went straight into training for the Central Intelligence Agency while still in Miami Dade Country Jail. His astonishing memory more than made up for his dyslexic writing problem. He was to morph into a Cuban citizen called David Montez.

"No esta mal," was Riley's observation when he saw himself in the mirror as David Montez, wearing his brown hair smoothed back off his face, a summery short-sleeved shirt and a thin layer of fake tanning lotion to leave a natural tint on his fair skin. And he was right—he didn't look bad. Dave wasn't one for pampering himself with products, but he had to be a credible young Cuban for his big CIA mission. He had to nail the image, the walk, the accent and the all-round-know-how. No detail was to be overlooked, he had been warned by the Feds throughout his two-month training program during his incarceration. How he wished he could phone home and crow to people on his old stomping ground about his new role, but the CIA had made it plain that he was to keep his mouth shut or else.

Only Lenny and James knew what was going on and almost every day they eagerly asked Dave for an update.

"When's the Firm getting us out of here, man?" whispered James, who was desperate to be moved from his cell, which he now shared with a redneck who had furrowed home-made Swaztika tattoos into his forearms with a smuggled razor and blue ink from a ballpoint pen.

James and Lenny had just about scraped through the Feds IQ test so they knew that Dave, being the star player in this set up, had to give them the nod as far as any future plans went.

"All in good time, guys. You'll see," Dave promised. When it came to his friends he liked to stand by his word. He worked harder than ever during the program.

The finishing touch to his slick Cuban ensemble was his newly grown handlebar moustache which was considered the height of style in Latin America and was not an uncommon sight in America itself in 1960. Looking in the mirror in his fully furnished CIA-owned apartment that was based on prison grounds while he awaited his imminent release, Dave thought it was going to be fun, playing this David Montez guy the Feds had been turning him in to. In fact, he kind of liked his reflection and the feel of his new facial hair that brushed over his top lip. It made him appear more mature than his years and gave him an air of authority—or even sophistication he imagined.

Dave had been briefed, coaxed and drilled relentlessly by the Feds. He had pored over books and tapes and had learned fluent Spanish until he once said that he even dreamt in the language. It was a grueling two months, but he easily passed the program and excelled in every given subject or exercise, whereas others like him had flunked out miserably and had languished back in jail cells, serving out their original full sentences.

Now that he had important people to impress, Dave soaked up new information faster than any straight "A" college student. It seemed there was nothing he didn't now know about Cuban history, art, music and current affairs.

"Go on, James…ask me something about Cuba." Dave's eyes were wide with enthusiasm as he and his two buddies whispered in the prison cafeteria. "Anything."

"Like what?" James shrugged.

"I dunno—anything you like."

James frowned. "Erm…who's the most famous Cuban music artist of the last twenty years?"

A smile twitched on the corners of Dave's lips. "Perez Prado," he said and then his hands suddenly shot up in the air and he groaned, "C'mon, man, ask me something more difficult this time will ya?"

AFTER HIS TRAINING, HE felt that infiltrating Castro's regime was going to be a cinch, but then Dave said that about everything he decided to get involved. There was nothing he loved more than taking on new personas and disguises and his latest role as CIA operative had Dave's pulse racing faster than anything else had in the two decades he had been on earth. He was at the end of his training and was raring to go.

In late summer 1960, when Dave, Lenny and James were released from jail with their extortion charges expunged, they were on orders to await further instruction from the Feds. Dave happily agreed and went straight back to his old life, doing what he knew best. He partied with different girls, stayed in cheap motels or with whomever he was dating at the time and hung out on the beach with Owen and Eaton, drinking beer, smoking weed and avoiding getting proper jobs. They even held up an odd 7-Eleven or drugstore when the mood took them even though they didn't have to as they were now well-paid government operatives.

There were no pay checks—only cash and this suited Dave just fine. Payment came discretely, like on the day Riley was on an errand, rushing through the crowds on Flagler Street in Downtown Miami, past large department stores and movie houses, when someone bumped into him. Two blocks later he put his hand in his jacket pocket and discovered nine-hundred-and-sixty dollars cash in a wad of twentys.

Although Dave was happy getting paid to hang out, and even cut a record or two, he was eager to make his mark and ready to join the Castro assassination campaign. The campaign was headed by mobster Frank Sturgis, right-hand man to Chicago's Sam Giancana, as well as one-time boss of Havana's former lucrative gambling center, Tampa's chief mobster Santos Trafficante, Jr.. Dave fantasized how famous he'd be if it was he who eliminated Castro after so many before had failed. With the Agency behind him, Riley's life was about to step up to a whole new level.

FOUR

A COMPULSIVE LIAR, RILEY could not be caught in a falsehood because he did not know how to tell the truth. If he believed something at the time he said it, Riley could make anyone believe it. Short and scrawny, Riley appeared incapable of getting anything right, hardly the type that either the CIA or the Mob would hire. And so, Riley's very unlikeliness then qualified him as precisely the right man for the CIA's operation headed by Maheu.

It was the second day of March 1960 when Sheffield Edwards, CIA Director of Security confided to Robert Maheu in the former's D.C. office, "It takes a lot to get Eisenhower mad—but he's mad as hell right now."

"Understandably so," Maheu replied, knowing that Sheffield referred to Castro's ever more hostile statements about the U.S. in those Radio Havana broadcasts. It was made clear he had, since seizing power a year and three months earlier, veered from democratic liberator to something of a socialist to hardcore communist, as such vulnerable to what American spies knew to be overtures as to setting up nuclear weapons, pointed at the United States merely 90 miles away.

"It'll come as no surprise to you that we've had our agents down there attempting to undermine Castro for the better part of a year. Now, we must kick it up a notch."

"And you believe I can be of service?" Maheu asked as he considered the situation. Though he'd left the FBI in 1947 to open offices as a private consultant and investigator, first in Washington and, after considerable success, California.

"Yesterday, Dick Bissell asked me to come up with someone who might put us in contact with members of the corporation that owns the gambling casinos in Havana." By that, Edwards meant the Mafia, even though the intimacy of his office as a government official hesitated to openly say such a thing. As for Bissell, the creator of JMARC, a covert action program against the Castro regime convinced that Castro needed to be removed before any invasion, he, as Maheu knew now, served as the CIA's Deputy Director for Plans. Word to strike hard and fast would have reached Bissell from Allen W. Dulles, the current Director of the CIA after Eisenhower ordered Dulles to do something.

"Anyway," Edwards continued, "I ran through some names and yours jumped out at me."

Once Maheu won over Howard Hughes as a client, it had become necessary for him to spend a great deal of time in Nevada. During off-hours in Vegas, Maheu visited the casinos, owned and run by those businessmen likewise in charge of similar properties in Havana. Mobsters, of course, but as private citizen Maheu no longer had to report directly to J. Edgar Hoover and he made it a point to mind his own business. Some of the rough fellows Maheu rubbed elbows with between 1955 and 1960, he knew, divided their work year between six months in Nevada and another six in Cuba, to make certain the two operations continued on a level of parity, until Castro took power, quickly closed the casinos, only to do an about face by reopening them. Still, tourists were afraid to fly down, causing the Mob to lose one-hundred million dollars a year from the casino business alone, plus lucrative returns from prostitution and drugs. Simply put, Castro had proved every bit as intolerable to the Mafia as he had to the United States Government. While the old adage about killing two birds with one stone did not apply, it might be both possible, even necessary, to kill one bird with two stones. Yes! If such parties were going to be brought in on this, Maheu certainly was the man who could make the contacts.

"Tell me Shef—up until now, have your strategies involved any of these other people, or did you assign only Agency men to do something about the Castro problem?"

"CIA professionals only, up until right now."

"Aren't they the best at what they do?" asked Maheu

"Sure. The problem is, Castro's own security got their hands on a list of our agents. They can spot one of our guys coming a mile away so we need to try something else."

"Truthfully Shef, I think it's a bad idea."

"You don't think they can be trusted?"

"It's not that. They consider themselves men of honor. If they agree to something, they'll see it through."

"What's the problem, then?"

"We'd be setting a precedent here that I don't think is healthy for the country. Government agents in league with the..."

"You've heard the old expression, 'an enemy of my enemy is

my friend?'"

"Sure. But I don't necessarily believe it to be true. We're supposed to be shutting them down, not..."

"That's the FBI's job. We're the CIA."

"Then it's okay to keep the governmental body's left hand from knowing what the right hand is up to?"

"I know it sounds crazy. Ever since the Kefauver Crime Commission began its work in 1950, there's been a concerted effort to bring down the Mob."

"Yet we'd be justifying the Mob's right to exist."

"Does that mean you won't help out?"

"Before I answer Shef, you have to keep in mind that if they do pull it off, from that moment actually, from the moment you first have me, or anyone else communicate with them, the CIA is in bed with the Mob—permanently!"

"I've thought about that," Edwards sighed.

"Are you comfortable with it?"

"Hardly! But these are troubling times. Comfort is not my immediate aim."

"Well, I'll do whatever you ask, but I have to draw the line somewhere and here it is. You've got to guarantee me we'll remove Castro without eliminating him."

Both men knew what Maheu meant: bring Castro down, but not kill him.

"Agreed." The two shook hands across Edwards' desk.

Edwards instructed Maheu to put the project on a back burner and go about his everyday business. Edwards didn't ask what jobs Maheu performed for them because, clean or dirty, he didn't want to know. After all, Maheu, since leaving the FBI after five years of service, had already been enlisted by the Agency to do several less than pure chores, undertaken in the name of national security. Maheu meanwhile did as instructed. When work brought him to Vegas, he consciously cultivated relations with Mob boys, deciding on one as his future contact when Shef eventually called and explained that he'd been going over plans with Bissell, Dulles, and J.C. King, Chief of the CIA's White House Division, for more than five months, so that when the first phase of what now had officially been tagged *Operation 40* went into operation, things would run smoothly. Though Maheu knew King to be a dependable man, he was not happy so many people had been brought into what, in his view, should remain a highly secretive affair. But he'd given his word, so there was no going back. Maheu felt sick when he learned that Gen. Charles Pearre Cabell, Chief of Air Force Intelligence, would also be briefed. When Maheu wailed that the widening circle of high-level participants must be curtailed, Edwards insisted that "the Old Soldier is alright." Cabell had been persuaded to accept a position as Deputy Director of the CIA while remaining employed as a four-star general at the Pentagon. This whole thing, Maheu would later recall thinking, is veering out of control! The CIA and the military? Once we also involve the Agency men, anything can happen!

Like Bob Maheu, James P. O'Connell had been a Special Agent for the FBI before he became involved with the CIA. Unlike the now-entrepreneurial Maheu, O'Connell had joined, serving as Chief Operational Support Division, Office of Security, Edwards decided to remove himself as much as possible from the work Maheu would be doing so as not to get his own hands dirty and appointed O'Connell as the "case officer" assigned to facilitate the "special intelligence operation" in any way Maheu found him useful. Though O'Connell enthusiastically greeted Maheu and appeared sincere while offering to serve as Bob's right hand, the man who had promised Edwards he would "get the job done" felt vaguely betrayed at having been passed off to someone else. A short while after committing to the project, Maheu's gut warned him this whole thing was already doomed to failure.

As Maheu and O'Connell prepared for their important September 23 meeting in Miami, Edwards held open round table discussions with members of the Agency, asking agents to offer up any ideas, however improbable, to take out Castro.

One hit on a bizarre scheme that held everyone's attention, the CIA would send an operative down to Havana, have the person convince Castro's minions he defected to serve the 'Cause.' This volunteer would lie and say he'd been involved in broadcasting back in the states and ask to help out whenever Castro spoke over Radio Havana. As an American, they would naturally be wary, always searching the man for hidden weapons, though he would carry none. The plan—destroy Castro's credibility with the Cuban people. The man they would send would insist on cleaning the studio, spraying air freshener about. Over time, this would come to seem a harmless ritual. Eventually, he would spray the studio with some substance that would cause Castro to grow disoriented. Cuba's leader would make a fool of himself live, on-air, setting into motion the beginning of the end to his regime. Meanwhile the perpetrator would slip away to some waiting escape vehicle.

"Seems reasonable, said Edwards. What chemical did you have in mind?"

"Lysergic acid is the official name. The government agency

that's been testing it, calls the stuff LSD."

"We'll have to check if it's dependable. If we do go with this, how do you suggest we get the stuff over there?"

"It'll be tough. Castro has just appointed a truly brilliant guy, Fabian Escalante, to head that agency."

"How about this?" someone else suggested. "Suppose we stage a skyjack. The pilot must appear to be some average guy though secretly paid by us. Accompanying him would be a recruit who has no previous connection with the CIA. Some obscure man who'd like to do his government a big favor, wants and needs the money he'd get, and hungers for some dangerous adventure in his life."

"Great. Only, where do we find such a man?"

"Let's all of us work on that."

One week later Edwards reached a decision. Though LSD had to be abandoned owing to what Edwards learned was its unpredictable impact could be heightened clarity rather than disorganization, the notion of a skyjack remained alive. Edwards discussed this with Jake Esterline, head of the Cuba task force, and Bissell. But the whole thing came down to finding a way to come up with a single individual willing to try just about anything.

"I think I've got it," Edwards announced. "Bob Maheu has already established a Mob connection, so we've got that. Now, no Agency man is going to risk his neck on a plan as far fetched as this. On the other hand, they like us to hire independant contractors to run all kinds of sleazy little jobs. A person who would do such stuff is precisely what we want."

"Alright," Esterline countered, "but what we have in mind is more risky than, say, blackmail. A guy gets caught trying that, he goes to jail. If picked up for messing with Castro? They'd kill him.

Only a fool would..."

"The man we're looking for is foolish—not stupid." Bissell said. "A truly stupid man couldn't be counted on. How about some street-smart guy, who knows how to get the job done but is drawn to dangerous situations? Loves them!

"Okay, let's say he's out there," Esterline sighed. "Where do we find him?"

"In jail," Edwards announced. The room fell silent. "Think about it. Some guy who has been running odd-jobs for the Mob, perhaps down Miami way. We already have George there, training Cuban refugees for a possible invasion by sea. Why not have him visit some local constabulary, see if maybe there are any guys fit the profile? Offer them the chance to get out, make a wad of dough to boot, and show their patriotic loyalty?"

"Fine. We'll tell George to bring one of the Mob boys along with him to pick the right man."

The problem turned out not to be finding the man they needed, but picking among the many volunteers who offered their services. George visited various jails with John F. Stewart, a Mob man who had recently arrived in Florida. He reported to Santos Trafficante in Tampa, who had informed him about Maheu and their new CIA connection. Stewart made it a point to introduce himself to George, Stewart not only agreed to join his manhunt, but took obvious delight in doing so. Several candidates were already well known to him as Trafficante briefed Stewart on operatives shortly before the first staged airborne hijacking took place.

"My beard," Fidel Castro swaggeringly stated in a TV interview, "means many things to my people." Though he did not choose to offer specifics, most listeners knew what he meant.

Shaggy, unkempt, possibly dirty, Castro's facial hair represented his rebellion against all the white-bread values America held most dear during the Eisenhower era. Here was a rebel, maverick, non-conformist. If he resembled anything it was a member of The Beat Generation, those equally squalid drop-outs from mainstream society who had grown disenchanted with postwar U.S. policy. Every upstanding suburbanite hated what was referred to as Beatniks. That term a combination of what such people called themselves and Soviet spacecraft Sputnik, launched into orbit on October 4, 1957, leaving the U.S. far behind in the U.S. race for space against the Russians.

How better to turn Castro into a figure of ridicule than by eliminating this signature item from his appearance? A naked-faced Fidel would look humorous to them and us. No one can respect or fear what they find funny.

And so began a two-month crusade to de-beard the Cuban leader. The first fake skyjacker carried with him a box of cigars laced with thallium salts, which the CIA's scientists insist would do the job. The perpetrator would land his captured plane, send the kidnapped pilot flying back home, then be accepted as a defector. He would worm his way into Castro's inner circle and, when the time felt right, offer Fidel a cigar, then scurry away. No sooner had The Beard breathed deeply than his nickname would no longer apply. No one took into account Castro's considerable sophistication to tobacco. He took one whiff and knew something was wrong. The cigars were disposed of and the volunteer whisked off to El Principe.

Shortly thereafter, following another reported theft of a commercial airplane, the next volunteer found work at the Havana

Hilton. Despite Castro's nonchalant attitude toward fashion, it was well known that he left his shoes outside his suite every night to be shined. Once the agent talked himself into this very job, he'd scatter thallium salts in the shoes, the idea being the chemicals would be absorbed right through Castro's socks and into his skin. Next morning, Fidel took one look at his shoes, saw white powder spread across their insides, and yelped for the employee responsible to be arrested. From then on, defectors from the U.S. were no longer greeted with a hero's welcome, as David Thomas Riley and his compatriots would learn in time.

"Everything's changed," Sheffield Edwards told Robert Maheu on November 22, 1960, some eight months after their only previous face-to-face meeting, fourteen days following the election of John Fitzgerald Kennedy to the Presidency.

"I'm listening," Maheu nervously responded.

"Ike was Ike and JFK is JFK. Nearly two months to go before he takes office and already he's changed the plan."

"You're scaring me, Shef."

"Brace yourself! Undermining Castro is no longer an option. Jack told Bissell, Bissell told me, and now I'm telling you the operative word is elimination."

"You swore that was not in the mix."

"Times change."

Both men knew without needing to actually say the word that from this moment on, the strategy would be to kill rather than disorient Fidel Castro.

"And it'll be Mob boys or some characters they farm the job out to who'll be expected to pull it off?"

"Right."

"Shef, have you heard the same rumors I have?"

Edwards nodded yes. Maheu could only be referring to a widely held belief that Kennedy's father Joseph had used his son's growing friendship with Frank Sinatra to connect with crime boss Sam Giancana. As a result the Mob, if this rumor were true, had arranged for JFK to carry key Chicago districts, making electoral victory inevitable.

"I know these people, you don't. With them, a deal is a deal. There can't be any reneging on promises, or they might just..." Maheu couldn't finish his sentence, so concerned was he about possible consequences of any double-dealing.

"You know me, Bob. I'd never..."

"It's not you I'm worried about." Edwards understood completely.

Maheu was not concerned about him, Bissell or Esterline. Maheu worried about the same thing Edwards did. The new wild card, with that charmingly cynical look in his eyes that made you wonder what JFK was really up to. And just how far he dared go as to manipulating people to his own ends, whatever they might be.

"Got you. Still, there are some solid reasons why this would be to our advantage. If the process were undertaken by these gentlemen, that would give us a...how to say it?... cover story. We want Castro gone and so do they. If your Vegas friends agree to complete the sort of job they are so expert at, we would of course pay them generously to do so. We should find ourselves in a no-lose situation."

"If any of their people then cried out that we were involved, we'd simply deny, deny, deny."

"Who would the American public believe? Mobsters or a

trusted government agency?"

Edwards shrugged, "If they fail, we're no worse off than we were before."

"If they succeed, everybody wins!"

"Can I sleep on it?"

Sheffield Edwards rose and stepped around his desk, warmly dropping an arm around Maheu's shoulder as he guided the visitor to the door. "I wouldn't have it any other way."

Castro, whom Maheu despised, threatened the U.S. If he did allow Russia to install atomic bombs, as many in government feared would happen, how many American lives might be lost so this one man might go on living? Maheu didn't even need to think of the mass destruction that might occur if Castro weren't removed. He loved his country and adored its people. If only one life, a single American life might be saved, how could Maheu say no? All night he wrestled with the shades of gray. Perhaps the days when moral matters presented themselves in black and white ended with the last good war. No matter how much Maheu longed for those days to return, he knew he now inhabited a different world. We were now involved in an altogether different sort of war. Still, war is war.

There was no doubt in Maheu's mind whose side he came down on. When he finally called Shef early the next morning, Maheu knew that from the moment this was broached, there had been only one possible answer he could offer.

The CIA decided botulin remained the best means possible, calling their man in Florida, George, to make contact with his Mob connection there and once again call on for the right man or woman for the job.

—Another perfect fool.

FIVE

ECLECTIC, FRANK ANTHONY STURGIS decided was the term that best described Havana's architecture. At mid-morning, he had stood on that craggy rock tourists so loved to mount and gazed out at the simple, understated El Morro lighthouse. As he strolled along the Malecon, then on to Habana Vieja, the historic old city, Sturgis marveled at the diversity of styles, each reflecting an era that had come and gone during the city's 400 year-old-history. Now, on this sunny siesta hour, Sturgis (or more correctly the man who had gone by that name for the past eight years) had plenty of time to search for the perfect word as he and Dave hunched over a small table at a humble café located kitty-corner to Plaza de la Cathedral. A hundred or so feet away, the immense baroque building that lent its name to this place, cut high into the sky, flanked by several crumbling palaces left over from Colonial days; each offering some uniquely lovely contrast to the area's dominating centerpiece.

"When will that dumb broad show up—on this day of all days?" Dave complained.

Sturgis glanced at his watch—2:30PM already. Nicky the Courier, with his green eyes glowing, had stopped by precisely on time, handing Frank the expected packet at 1:45. The Kraut, as Sturgis mentally referred to the young woman who should have arrived half--an-hour earlier, clearly was pulling her how-late-can-I-make-my-grand-entrance-without-causing-you-to-throw-a-tantrum bit. That was to be expected. Sturgis had never known a beautiful woman who didn't believe her looks granted her the right to keep the whole wide world waiting. Trying to contain his mounting frustration. How dare she be late on this all important occasion?

To temper himself, Frank Sturgis forced himself to consider those varied buildings he'd passed while strolling here from the harbor. The influences ranged from ancient Moors, Spanish, and Italians to the art-nouveau styles so trendy during the 1920s. Thanks to a course he'd taken at Virginia Polytechnic Institute while studying on the G.I. Bill following his service in the Marines during WWII, Sturgis or Frank Angelo Fiorini back then, appreciated the array of approaches in a way the casual visitor did not.

"If she doesn't show, what will I..." Suddenly, there she was, a vision of loveliness as always, floating toward him from around a corner and down an angular boulevard as if she stepped not over the pavement but glided on air itself. Smiling broadly, basking in her confidence that one look at her female splendidness would erase all angry emotions. If only there were time for sex, few women Sturgis had bedded were capable of the heat he'd experienced with her, that cool-as-an-iceberg surface dissolving the moment The Kraut hit the sheets. Not today, though. Not for him, but 'The Beard'—likely. As Sturgis reached into his pocket for the cellophane wrapped package of blue pills Nicky the Courier instructed him to hand to her, without one word passing between them, Sturgis's mind considered the sleek killing machine he had transformed the giddy girl he'd first met a year ago, she then barely 18. Now? Like something out of an Ian Fleming novel. One of those deliciously duplicitous dames, elegant and deadly, those fictional female agents who most enjoyed sex with a man when she knew the entire time of their pleasure together, doomed to die at discretion when their lovemaking ended. Yes, Sturgis thought as he rose and seemingly shook hands with an unexpected friend passing by, Lorita Morenz did rate as a real-life Bond woman, if with a touch of the era's underage dream girl, Lolita, thrown in.

"WHO IS HERE?" THE moment that Fidel Castro stepped into his suite at the Havana Hilton on November 30, 1960, he sensed at once someone had entered earlier and now awaited him in the darkness. Instinctually, Castro's hand reached for the wall switch to flip on the light and learn who might be lurking here, about to confront and assassinate him. Swift thinking prevented Fidel from doing that as he realized, so long as both remained in the dark, the intruder could not perceive him any more clearly than he could the hidden figure. An instinct urged him to turn and rush out the half open door, back down the hallway. Make a mad dash for the stairs, hurry away from this place that suddenly smelled of death. But his brain rejected that. Castro sensed, when silhouetted against the light that poured in from hallway, he'd offer an easy target. Perhaps such a panicked flight was just what the potential gunman hoped for.

Quickly regaining his nerve, Castro kicked the door closed behind him, plunging the living room into darkness as the window shades had all been drawn. How anyone could have slipped past security seemed beyond belief. But might one of his trusted bodyguards have been susceptible to bribery? Was there no one left in the world Castro could trust?

"Calm down, Fidel. It's only me."

Footsteps in the dark, swiftly moving toward him, were distinguishable. Every person exhibits his or her own gait, as much a signature as a fingerprint. Plus he experienced the familiar pungent scent of mango, revealing the presence of a perfume he well knew. Then Castro felt the slender arms embrace him as had happened so many times before, followed by a kiss in the night, sensuous yet cruel.

"Lorita?"

"Yes, Fidel. Your own personal Lolita."

She stepped away from him and flipped on the lights. He in turn marveled at the 19-year-old's figure, displayed for him now in a simple silver sheath that shimmered with her every move.

Lorita Morenz, the German-born beauty from Bremen who had made her way to Cuba, sought him out in the hills, then announced she would be the divorced Castro's lover for as long as he liked. "I must share the magic moment in world history that is about to occur. Be at your side when the hour of triumph happens," she told him then.

She might be an agent from Batista, assigned to kill me. Or even from the American Mob or CIA—a lethal Lolita. I should send her away at once he thought. But, she is too lovely to do that. If my fate is to die in her arms, so be it.

Fidel had taken Lorita as his mistress. Together they had entered Havana after the spectacular New Year's Eve Revolution.

"How did you get in?" he stumblingly inquired.

"With this."

She held high the key that he had given her on their first night together before the feeling between them slowly soured. Lorita had yelped like a slapped puppy when he dared inform her that, now that he was indeed supreme leader, perhaps it might be time to reconcile with his estranged wife Mirta. Whether that could be managed or not, he absolutely had to bring his son, young Fidel, there to live with him, particularly as the legendary newsman Edward R. Murrow planned to conduct a 'Person to Person' interview with him for American TV later that year.

"But I want to sit beside you during the interview."

"Lorita, please. Be reasonable."

"Reasonable? If you truly loved me, you would want the entire world to see me with you and know the truth."

"Even a communist must deal with appearances."

"You're a phony. Everything I thought you were is only a show. You're no better than the man you ousted."

At that moment, Castro, his ego deflated and his mind grasping that she had just spoken a truth he lived in daily denial, slapped her hard across the face. He knew this to be a tragic mistake even before the action could be completed, yet he'd felt powerless to stop himself. The tiny brunette emitted a shriek that resounded through the room, likely the entire hotel.

Castro knew that momentarily guards would come running to check on his well-being, but before that could happen, Lorita had leaped up off the couch and vaulted out the door, past his trusted

Puto Valle and other stunned bodyguards who threw themselves
up against the corridor walls, allowing the raging banshee to pass,
yet to return in only a moment later. Theatrics was one of Lorita's
gifts.

"Why did you come back?" Castro asked as Lorita marched
to the far side of the room. There she entered the bedroom they
had shared for a glorious period, those intense bouts of sex deeply
missed by this prominent world leader who had but two admitted
weaknesses: fine Cuban cigars and gorgeous women from
anywhere. Young women in particular. Lorita had been seventeen
when he first met her. A child-woman. Why do men so desire them?
Castro did not know the answer to that. He only understood that,
like all men, her youth appealed to him as much as her remarkable
looks. Yes, he had read Vladimir Nabokov's controversial novel
while a law student at the university.

"Guess."

That was so like Lorita! Flirtatious, enticing and always eager
to play little games, particularly with the man in her life. Once
she had insisted he dress like a 1930s Chicago gangster, Lorita his
flapper girlfriend. On another occasion Lorita arrived with a box of
costumes containing a pirate outfit for him, harem girl attire plus a
purple boa for herself. She insisted he play out scenes with her that
derived from old movies she'd seen, loved, wished to be a part of,
dreamed of disappearing into.

"I want life to be the way it appears in Hollywood films," she
once admitted to Fidel.

"Your wish is my command," he once declared. Either forgive
my rash act, which I've already apologized for, and come back to
me—or."

"Or what, Fidel?" Castro made no conscious effort to follow her and step into the adjoining bedroom. He was drawn as if by a magnet. His feet taking him where his mind dared not go.

"Kill me," he admitted, entering. Lorita had slipped out of her sheath, which now lay in a heap on the floor. She wore only a combination of silk and velvet lingerie, both Midnight black, presenting herself as he most loved to gaze upon her. Lorita had curled up on the bed like some self-serving Persian cat, smiling in a way that rendered the great man powerless.

"And which," she laughed, "do I appear ready to do?"

"Kiss me. Kill me. Perhaps first one, then..."

"Come," Lorita invited, spreading her elegant arms outward, "and meet your destiny."

"So," Lorita asked when the lovemaking was finished, "are you alive or dead?"

"In a manner of speaking," Castro laughed, "dead."

"Le petite morte, eh? But your great fear has not occurred, Fidel. There may not be much of you—any man—left when I am finished ravishing my lover. Still, you live."

Even in the dark bedroom, enough light from the streets below passed through one window where the shade had been only half drawn for Lorita to make out Fidel's frown.

"The night is still young. And I have a feeling your little drama is but partially played out."

"You know me too well," Lorita laughed. Not a happy, but bitter, rather aloof. "And yet you allowed me to join you here. Why, if you..."

"I could not send you away." He ran his hands over her tight, hard frame. "You knew I would not be able to."

"Yes," Lorita coldly answered. "I knew that."

"Yet it was important to you that I say so."

"A woman wants to hear such words spoken."

"I don't—"

"Understand? Of course not. No man ever understands how a woman thinks—or feels."

She sat, above him, a 19-year-old beauty, slender and seemingly vulnerable, staring down at one of the world's most important men, hated and loved, worshipped and feared. Knowing that at this moment his fate rested in her hands.

"Men are such fools," she thought. "Thank God for that, or what would we women do? Even now I see, in his eyes, desire mixed with horror. Thrilled to discover whether he's going to live or die. And if I should choose to kill him, there's nothing he could do, though this rugged beast with a beard could break me like a twig. But he can't. Because I'm beautiful. That is what makes him—all men—vulnerable."

"How does it feel, Lorita, to conquer me?"

"Good, Fidel. My flesh tingles with satisfaction."

"I can see that," he sighed, peering up into her liquid eyes. Your body is alive, in a way it was not before."

"And yours?"

"Dead, for all intents and purposes."

She leaned down, brushing her dark hair across his face, again and again. "And perhaps, in a moment or two, dead also in the eyes of the world."

"You would kill me after what we've just experienced?"

"Well," she giggled like a naughty little girl.

"I certainly wouldn't have killed you before." With that she leaned down and kissed him. A split second before Lorita pulled her mouth up and away, she bit his lower lip. When Fidel yelped with pain, her body experienced a sudden sensation not unlike the multiple orgasms that had swept over her during their two hours of desperate sex.

"That hurt," Castro whined.

"It was supposed to," she tantalizingly said before slipping off of him, standing upright on the floor. Lorita grabbed her black bikini bottom and slipped into it with a graceful movement that suggested a worldliness beyond her years. It seemed to Fidel that she purposefully half-dressed when she did not bother to also restore her black bra to the rack of soft flesh it earlier contained. This allowed her breasts, large for so small a girl, to swing provocatively with every move. Castro watched them, amazed at the infinite variety of ways in which such a women could, with the simplest gesture, reduce a man to rubble.

"I'll be back," she whispered tantalizingly. Lorita reached for her purse and tip-toed toward the adjoining bathroom, where she often cleaned herself following sex with Fidel Castro when their romance had been at its height.

"To finish the job?"

"Oh, Fidel," she sighed just before disappearing into the bathroom, "stop already. I mean, it was fun playing out that little scenario. Something out of a spy novel. We both know that was just our little game for the evening."

"Was it?" he called after Lorita as she firmly closed the bathroom door. "Then why did you come back to me?"

With the bathroom light on and the door locked, Lorita reached into her purse and pulled out her ovular bottle of cold cream. Here was where she had hidden the botulin pills she would now use to kill Castro. Lorita knew her Beard well enough to guess, though, that on some level, he longed for it. During their time together, the lumbering giant, always appearing so supremely confident in khaki fatigues while hiding behind that thick beard, had revealed so many of his secret insecurities and private fantasies. No man sensed his mortality more than Castro. He did not fear death itself, only dying from a bullet or knife wielded by some male assassin. One obsession from his youth, though, had been to expire in the arms of a dark angel, some belle dame sans merci. To him, such a death would be a victory, not a defeat.

He thought, "Let my death be a desirable one. In the arms of Lorita? My God! What a way to go!"

Lorita opened the cold cream jar and reached inside to remove the botulin pills. Such a wonderful inspiration it had been to hide them in here! Even the oh, so careful Valle had not thought to look in this unlikely spot when he had inspected Lorita several hours earlier, searching for some more obvious weapon on her person, after allowing her to pass, gloating at the thought of the pleasure in store for his beloved leader on that night. In a moment Lorita would, pills in hand, exit the bathroom, rejoin Fidel on the bed, slip the botulin into the glass of water which her lover, always consumed by thirst, kept handy. She would hand him the glass, excitedly watching as he accepted the drink and again considered her closely, wondering if this were indeed his moment of truth. But he would drink; she had no doubt of that. He must learn if her surrendering of herself to him on this night had been a ruse. There was only one way to learn; that was to drink. So he would drink. Because the end of man is to know.

"Oh!" Lorita gasped as she realized that something had gone terribly wrong. The blue-tinted botulin pills, which she believed would remain soft yet solid in the white cream, had all decomposed. Lorita always assumed that their coating would be hard enough to maintain them here; she'd been told if they were exposed to extreme heat they might dissolve and be unusable. Lorita hadn't figured on them being susceptible to a cool context. Now, though, the blue color had spread all through the white cream. Lorita could hardly expect Fidel to swallow any of that awful looking mixture; the pills would have dissolved in water and not been susceptible to taste. Only an aftertaste, but by then it would be too late. Lorita stood staring at the jar. A moment before, she had believed herself the perfect assassin, ready to finish off her prey. Now she felt like a child, inept and naive. So Lorita did what little girls do in just such situations: She sat down on the toilet and cried.

Is that Lorita sobbing? Castro wondered. Yes, I'm sure it is. For a moment, he considered rising from the bed and going to the bathroom to comfort her in whatever female snit Lorita had managed to work herself into. Perhaps she cried because she really did love him and, after rediscovering sex with Fidel, Lorita sensed she would not be able to leave him again; from this day forth willingly, his secret mistress as he had suggested a year ago on that day when she walked out of his life. Then it occurred to him, this might be something more cryptic, closer to the nightmarish fantasies he'd experienced the entire time they'd spent in each other's arms. So he remained still, for the better part of an hour, listening to her sob from behind the closed bathroom door. Sooner or later, she must emerge. Then he would know from the look in Lorita's eyes what truly had transpired.

"Oh, God," Lorita whined as, all the previous style and sophistication gone from her movements, she at last opened the door and staggered over to the bed, dropping down beside Fidel, weeping. "I could fuck up anything."

"Except a fuck," he ventured.

"Yes. The one thing I'm always good at."

Castro roared with laughter. Even at a traumatic moment like this, Lorita could be counted on to crack a smart gag.

"What is it?" he whispered, stroking her hair.

Lorita pulled her tear-drenched face up from the pillow and confronted Castro. "You tell me."

For a moment, Fidel froze. "It's as I guessed. You came here tonight to kill me, didn't you?"

She shook her head yes.

"For yourself, and your false belief that I betrayed you in love? Or did you act as an agent for some interest?"

"Does it matter now?"

"To me? Very much."

"Well, Fidel, I won't tell you, even if you said that you would be willing to spare my life if I did." She sobbed again, this time, he realized, in self pity for what she believed he would shortly do to her.

"Just one moment, my darling," Castro said, reaching to the cabinet by his bed and opening a drawer. Wiping the wet residue from her face.

Lorita arched herself around so that she could see what he extracted. It was an automatic pistol. "Oh, God," she wailed. "I knew this was coming."

"Don't be silly," Castro gently reassured her. He pulled Lorita up to a sitting position so that she in her black bikini bottom and no bra straddled him, pinning the big man to the bed with her petite frame. Then he handed her the gun. She looked confused. He smiled.

"Go ahead. Your job was to kill me? Do it."

Castro pulled the gun toward his face, opened his mouth, lowered his lips on the barrel. If she did as told, the last thing on earth he would see were her wondrous breasts, sliding back and forth as she moved to find a solid position, tightening her grip on the trigger.

"Just like in the movies!" she roared.

Spy thrillers had already been filmed in Asia and Europe and from a report she'd heard were now to be produced by U.S. companies as well, they now believing the mainstream was ready to accept such kinky stuff. *Dr. No* would be the first.

Castro remained supremely calm through it all. That unnerved Lorita, but she readied herself to finish the job. Still, a minute went by, Lorita unable to complete what she'd arrived to do. Those pills would have allowed her to remain remote from the administration of death. To pull the trigger, see her lover's head explode, the blood and brains pouring out onto the pillow, splattering against the wall? It was, simply, too much. Hard as she tried to pull the trigger, Lorita found herself releasing her grip.

"I can't," she wailed, removing the barrel from Fidel's mouth. "Lord knows I want to. But I... can't."

"Of course you can't," Fidel said, offering a quirky smile. "No one can." He slipped the pistol from her hand and returned it to the drawer, which he closed.

"Now, what?"

"Now?—Leave."

"Just like that?" She snapped her fingers.

Castro nodded. Wanefully, Lorita pulled herself up off him and stood for a moment, glaring. Then she set about dressing herself, sniffling back tears the entire time. Once the silver sheath again adorned her stunning frame, Lorita gathered her things and made ready to leave, stepping by Fidel, then out the bedroom door and into the main room without a backward glance. There she stopped, returned, and pulled something from her purse.

"Here," she sniffed, dropping the key to his suite beside Fidel on the bed where he appeared relaxed, as if nothing out of the ordinary had happened.

"You won't be coming back, then?"

"Never."

"Will there be others?"

"That's not for me to say." She started to leave once more but again halted.

"When you said to me, 'no one can.' What did you mean?"

Castro smiled from ear to ear. "I am Fidel. My destiny is to guide Cuba into its future. That was written in the stars a million years ago. No one could interfere with that. Not even a woman as willful, wicked, and wondrous as you."

Lorita nodded, then slipped out of the room, the suite, the hotel, and his life.

It's the Mob, Castro thought as he lay there in the darkness. the Mafia just declared war!

Why is it we always think of the perfect thing to say after we're gone and it's too late to get in the last word? For years, after her hurried exit, Lorita Morenz rolled over in her mind what she could have told Fidel on her way out. Never had she revealed to him that, when she first left Germany, at fifteen, truly a Lolita then, not only in looks but also age. She had not gone to Cuba directly, as she had lyingly told Fidel. Lorita headed first for Venezuela, there scheming to meet and seduce President Marcos Perez Jimenez, the country's right wing junta dictator. Though married, he had set her up in a suite at the Humboldt Hotel, overlooking Caracas, where they spent many a pleasurable hour until, in 1958, the communists staged a comeback and he had to run away to America, there awarded the Legion of Merit for his distinguished if doomed fight against "The Red Menace." Unfortunately, he took along his wife and family, but not Lorita, when he scurried away in the night. Guessing the next great Third World leader would likely be a communist, Lorita had decided to become mistress to such a person. Everyone insisted Fidel Castro was likely to emerge as the top Red leader, so off she trekked to Cuba, there proving that the unique beauty of a child-woman cuts across politics. If Lorita had thought to mention to Fidel he'd taken the castoff mistress of a near-fascist dictator as the great love of his life, that revelation, she knew would likely have killed him faster than botulism or a bullet.

For once, The Kraut not only showed up on time, but actually arrived before Sturgis for what would prove their final meeting. The place was once again at the humble café located kitty-corner to Plaza de la Cathedral, 24 hours after their silent meeting. He had listened to Radio Cuba all morning, then poured through the paper's first edition, noting that things were normal in Cuba today. Now she wept in his arms, spitting out bits and pieces of her failure. The Bond Girl all gone; the pretty child replacing her again.

Cold cream jar? Obviously The Kraut, aka Lorita Morenz,

Code-name: Lolita, would not be called upon again by the Agency. They must find some other way to kill Castro. As he sent her away, Frank Anthony Sturgis, aka Frank Angelo Fiorini, wondered whether she ought to be eliminated as a security risk. If so, he would do to her what she had tried to do with Fidel; bed the prey one more time. No, Sturgis decided. She seemed so pathetic now, he no longer wanted her, the girl's looks notwithstanding. Why kill such a klutz? Let her talk to anyone she chose; no man in his right mind would believe such a lovely train wreck. Let their Bremen-born babe go wherever she wished. Now, though, he must meet Nicky the Courier and inform him as to what had gone down, or rather, what had failed to go down.

"DAVE, WE ARE NOT giving up." Sturgis ordered, "I want you to take a waiter's job at one of Castro's favorite restaurants. The CIA produced a batch of Botulinum pills. They killed a couple of monkeys over two days without a trace of the poison. Fidel eats at this place at least twice a week, so there'll be no pressure. Just drop the poison in his soup whenever the time feels right. This has the blessing of Giancana, Trafficante, even the President and your CIA boss Robert Maheu."

—And yet another trap was set, but Castro inexplicably broke that routine and never showed up again at the lavish eatery.

SIX

A MAN OF QUIET confidence, yet one who understood things can go wrong, Richard M. Bissell, Jr., CIA's Deputy Director for Plans, spent most of that mid-April weekend in 1961 alone in his office waiting for the phone to ring. Knowing that when it did and he received firsthand reports from the front line of combat in an undeclared, and if Bissell's plan worked, an invisible war, then he'd ring up JFK and share the news. Considering Bissell's mixed opinions about Kennedy, he prayed all had gone well. Meanwhile, Bissell would stay in touch with Adlai Stevenson in New York. Our Ambassador to the United Nations had, in Bissell's mind, been one of the thornier elements in this affair. From day one, Bissell had feared what he referred to as the 'Egghead Factor' could merge as the loose screw in an otherwise perfectly functioning machine which Bissell had constructed. After receiving authorization from his boss, CIA Director Allen W. Dulles, who had spoken briefly with JFK, Bissell sent top outfit representative, Tracy Barnes flying off for an unexpected visit to Stevenson's office along Manhattan's East River. Barnes knew what Bissell had told him, which was what Dulles had said to Bissell and Kennedy to Dulles: "Get Stevenson behind this and he'll set the frosting on the cake of our Cuban adventure. But, what if things don't go the way they're supposed to down there is a what if, for the time being, we can't consider. Just make certain Stevenson grasps that what he says or does not say will likely determine the manner in which the world will perceive America for the remainder of the 20th century."

"I'll try."

"Don't 'try.' Do it!"

However huge Stevenson's moral conscience or however sincere his desire to be the most honest man in politics since Abe Lincoln, Barnes knew this came down to what was best, not for Adlai, but for his country. Would he accept the bitter pill and agree that in the grand scheme of things, Stevenson's reputation must be considered inconsequential compared to America's safety? The official line had long held that Stevenson knew nothing about the recruitment and training of Cuban exiles in Miami. Then again, only a blind, deaf oaf could remain oblivious to what took place in broad daylight, with no attempt at concealment. The Cuban Brigade's existence did crack the newspapers, particularly the *New York Times*, on several occasions. Deeply concerned he may have been seen as the first statesman to negatively refer to cowboy diplomacy.

STEVENSON HAD SEVERAL MONTHS previously called the White House in a panic and JFK's secretary set up a meeting. Part of the reason Kennedy had been elected, despite a rigid Catholic background, was that he'd cultivated a Teddy Roosevelt image, an intellectual rough rider, a man of word and deed. Though a loyal party member, as such eager to get behind any Democrat who could actually win the popular vote, Stevenson had tried to belie his own fears that what JFK offered qualified more as image than reality—the smart guy and tough guy aspects of a persona representing charisma over character.

"You know," the President said as they sat across from each other in the Oval Office, each sipping coffee, "when he couldn't slip off to golf, Ike used to take his mind off the cold war by slipping in here and reading Zane Grey novels."

"I'm aware Mr. President that he liked cowboy stories."

"Well, Adlai, I do, too. Except that I find those books awfully dated now."

"In all honesty, I don't read them."

Kennedy grinned knowing how much Stevenson enjoyed the serious novels of Updike and Cheever. "No, I didn't imagine you would. Personally, I like light reading. The frontier spirit, that sort of thing."

"In truth, Mr. President, isn't that more myth than reality? As someone who devours books on history I know..."

"Yes, yes. I'm sure you can rattle off all the facts, Adlai. I read history too. But I'm also a man of the people. And do you know where the masses get their ideas? About the wild west, as with everything else?"

Stevenson swallowed hard. "At the movies."

Kennedy winked and nodded. "Mrs. Kennedy and I enjoyed an advance screening of the new John Ford film several weeks ago."

Actually, the President caught the movie with Marilyn

Monroe. Their buddy Frank Sinatra had used his connections to set up a preview of the film's rough cut, but certainly didn't say so to Stevenson.

"*The Man Who Shot Liberty Valance.* Very Republican! John Wayne, Jimmy Stewart, that whole crowd. Looking long in the tooth, I might add. I think their whole era is just about over. Don't you?"

This turned out to be one of those rare times in his life when Stevenson felt like an ignoramus. "In truth? When I go to the movies, which is rarely, it's to see Bergman, Fellini ..."

"I like them, too, but I never can resist a good Western. Anyway, there's a line at the end that touched me deeply. All the way through, Jimmy Stewart believes he's killed a terrible bad man. Years after the event, he learns John Wayne did it. Blasted that son of a bitch Lee Marvin from an alley where The Duke had stationed himself."

Stevenson thought, "Why in the name of all that's holy is the President wasting time, rambling on about some dumb oater, when we should be discussing Cuba? Which is what I came here for!"

"Anyway," Kennedy continued, "years later, a newspaper man learns all of this when Stewart can't keep it inside any longer and admits what actually went down. Looks like the full story will find its way into print and ruin Stewart's career. He's an important United States senator now. If the truth gets out, his entire success in politics is based on a lie and he'll be destroyed. All the good he can achieve in Washington—over."

He's tooling me. he thinks, but can't resist, that Kennedy charm—he smiles that smile—Stevenson felt a need to say something, no matter how perfunctory.

"Apparently, this movie made a big impression on you."

"The point Adlai is it doesn't matter who pulled the trigger. Who the hell cares, once things are peaceful again for the town, which man did the actual shooting?"

"I...uh, perhaps not, Mr. President."

"Of course not." Kennedy knew he had won, his victory blazing away in those irresistible eyes.

"You know something else? While I was watching, I began to think about all of us today. That town, Wishbone, Knee Cap, whatever, seemed to me a microcosm of America. Not just our country as it was way back in pioneer days, but the United States, now!"

"Truthfully, Mr. President, I didn't come here today to talk about westerns or any other kind of movie."

"I know that, Adlai." Kennedy, about to close in for the kill, smiled sweetly. "Please, call me Jack. My friends do. I'd like to consider you a friend."

Adlai found himself capitulating. "Thank you, sir."

"No. I'm the one who should be thanking you for being a loyal friend, loyal Democrat—most of all, a loyal American."

"I try, sir."

"You do more than try. You get the job done. Now, you see, I've got an important job that has to be done. And you, Adlai, are the only man in America who can do it."

"I know. That's why I had to come here today."

"Of course. We'll talk about that in a moment. First, let me tell you the last line of that movie."

Stevenson wonders again, I've never heard of anyone being so influenced by a film.

"When the journalist realizes Stewart's reputation as the man who shot Liberty Valance is only a myth, guess what he does?"

Stevenson tried to figure out what was coming next, but couldn't. "He publishes the truth, I'd imagine?"

Kennedy chuckled. "That's what you'd do?"

"I'd like to believe so, if I were still a reporter."

"He tore the story up and threw it away."

That surprised, even shocked Stevenson. "Why?"

"Why not? What good would it have done to tell people ugly details when they already know a truth that makes them happy? When the legend becomes a fact, print the legend."

Now it was Stevenson's turn to pause, consider, and at last speak. "Do you believe he did the right thing?"

No hint of hesitation in JFK's voice: "I do."

Stevenson hesitated to consider, such hesitations had determined he would never be President.

"I'm not certain."

Kennedy leaned across the table, speaking in a gentle, conspiratorial tone. "The reason you're here today, Adlai, is that I want to make you grasp he did do the right thing—and in the coming weeks, so should you!"

THAT CONVERSATION HAD TAKEN place three months prior to the attack, first by air and then sea to land, on Cuba. One week before what those in the know referred to as *D-Day II*, Tracy Barnes arrived in New York to confer with Stevenson. His mission: Seal the deal Kennedy had initiated. No one believed that Tracy Barnes had anything remotely like the Kennedy charisma, least of all Barnes. Yet he was what all referred to as a good soldier, committed to the cause.

April 13, 1961, Manhattan's weather reported as overcast, dark gray skies above, only the slightest hint of sunshine occasionally cutting through. Stevenson stood by his window, peering down at the people. How deeply he cared about them. How fiercely he wanted to believe that the current President felt as committed to them as he did.

"We in Washington have an inkling," Barnes stated, plopped in a comfortable chair, gazing at Stevenson's back, "that a number of Cuban exiles will attempt to retake possession of their country. Some reports suggest it could happen in days. We don't know that for certain, though some of us, myself included, believe it will. If so, my guess is, this will begin late Friday or early Saturday, then be all over by Monday. At that time, Castro will be dead, Cuba in the hands of those native people who respect and appreciate us."

Momentarily, Stevenson stood as still as the proverbial statue. Barnes worried that this man he had patently lied to, lied by omitting that CIA agents would direct the mission while the sea-to-land invasion would be launched from U.S. Naval ships, might suffer a stroke. Barnes was about to approach Stevenson, sincerely concerned, when the silver-haired American ambassador slowly turned. To Barnes' shock, Stevenson looked as if he had been silently crying.

"Tell me precisely what it is you want of me."

"Mr. Stevenson, please." Not incapable of empathy, Barnes' heart went out, touched by this man's appearance and tone of voice. "You sound as if I'm Old Scratch himself, here to steal away your immortal soul."

"Ha!" Not the sort of person to laugh out loud, Adlai shocked Barnes with his outburst. "You nailed that one."

Barnes cautiously stepped forward. He'd had a little contact with this man before and respected him even if he considered Stevenson something of a milk-toast. He sensed the great depth of emotion, the code that Adlai, with his sweetly-sad face, lived by. "Mr. Ambassador, please keep in mind that, though there will be blood, all of this, if it does happen, will absolutely lead to a greater good."

"Sir, I do not doubt your intentions."

"Thank you! Then—"

"Who claimed that the road to hell is lined with them?"

"I—can't recall."

"No matter, only that it was said. And the eternal, horrible, tragic truth of that statement."

"We must do what we think is right."

"Don't tell me! I know. Because you, me, we are
the good guys."

Without hesitation, Barnes nodded. "Precisely."

"But you see," Stevenson continued, abruptly turning away, circling back behind his large, low desk. "I'm not so certain I believe in good guys or bad guys anymore, like I once did back during the war. Surely Hitler was a monster."

"Even as Castro is now."

Stevenson's eyebrows rose high. "Do you think so? I'm not certain. Make no mistake about it, I'd love to believe he is. And that opposing the bad, qualifies us as good. But let me say, lately, I have my doubts."

What pitiable eyes this man has, Barnes thought. The opposite of Kennedy's. JFK concentrates on reducing you to rubble with a look, concealing what's actually going on inside that self-serving head of his. This poor bastard, his eyes offer a wide open window into his soul. Barnes honestly regretted what he had to do. Nonetheless, it was his job. "I can tell you this much, Castro is bad for the U.S."

"Perhaps because we made him that way?"

"I can't answer that. In all honesty, I don't know that you're wrong there."

"So?"

"So! What I do know is what's past, right or wrong, is past. We live in the present. We are Americans. Like any nation, we must put our own survival first."

"Which means bringing down Castro?"

"That's a bit harsh. Let's say, rather, we will stand aside and allow our allies to accomplish that."

Then came the longest pause in their conversation. "I cannot argue against what you have said."

"Wonderful! That's all I need to..."

"I wasn't finished! Just so long as you give me your assurance, your absolute word of honor, that the United States will not, through either military or para-military units, assume any active part."

"I absolutely promise you we will not," Barnes lied straight-faced. He didn't like doing this but he did it.

Stevenson stared hard into Barnes's eyes, trying to tell if the man was speaking the truth. Unfortunately, he did not have the gift to make such calls. "You are here, I assume, as a representative not only of the President and the State Department, but also the CIA?"

"That is correct."

"As a member of that organization, can you swear to me, and in so doing, imply the honor of Dulles and the President, that this 'Operation' as you call it will be entirely managed and carried out by anti-Castro Cubans?"

Barnes was too savvy to hesitate before answering. "I can tell you that is absolutely the case," he lied. He was a man with a conscience. It didn't make him feel good to deceive so sensitive a person, but Barnes had pledged to Bissell that he would take care of this matter, so Barnes continued his barrage of lies: "The Cubans are on their own. They will fly from entirely abandoned airfields. And no U.S. representatives will be involved."

Stevenson had to curb a desire to cynically snicker, though in truth, cynicism was not a natural emotion in his make-up. "What is a man to do?" he suddenly asked, shaking.

"The right thing."

"Ah, but how do we know what's the right thing?"

A minute later Barnes was gone, leaving Adlai alone in his office, sobbing. The ambassador prayed he'd been told the truth. If he had any inkling that was not the case, he'd remain loyal to his basic values during whatever the next days might bring. He rolled the whole thing over in his mind, returning to the conversation he'd had with Kennedy three months earlier. Now, a part of what the President had said assumed center stage in Stevenson's consciousness. He'd flown home with that John Wayne story pounding in his brain, but before Adlai had been swiftly and politely escorted out, Kennedy segued back to where the discussion began, Ike and his Zane Grey novels. Most of them, Kennedy had mentioned offhand, centered around a righteous hero named Lassiter. The man with one name. A foreboding stranger who rode into town, as JFK recollected from reading a couple of those pulp fiction classics while at sea on P.T. 109.

"Funny, how heroes come and go. Today, I'd imagine only older people, from Ike's generation, reach for those books."

Kennedy opened his desk drawer and pulled out a paperback, tossing it to his guest.

"Have you read this?"

Confused, Adlai perused the cover. *Dr. No,* its title announced, by Ian Fleming. Below it, the image of a menacing looking man, suave, surly, self-possessed, cradling a gun. Stevenson guessed it to be a Baretta, though he knew precious little about firearms. The threatening character wore a perfectly tailored suit. On either side stood a beautiful woman, both in skimpy bikinis, one blonde, the other brunette. Each leggy girl assumed a stance at once regal and servile, a pair of queens conquered by this dominating male. All three situated on some a beach in Bermuda, or perhaps the Cayman Islands. Low on the cover, Stevenson read the tag-line: "Licensed to kill!" At last the Stevenson glanced up.

Kennedy chuckled. "No, I don't imagine you have. A friend, well, colleague, really more in league with my brother Bobby than myself, turned me on to it— pilot down in Florida.The fellow gave this copy to Bobby. Rumor has it that the book may soon be turned into a movie."

"It all looks a bit risqué for Hollywood."

"Good point, Adlai. Maybe what they can and can't do in movies is about to change. The point is this James Bond chap, in

my mind, rates as the contemporary equivalent of old-timers like
Lassiter. Instead of plodding along through sagebrush on a horse,
he zips across the continent in an Aston Martin. Kills without
compunction. Enjoys lovely women without feeling any need to
make a serious commitment."

Dawning on him all at once, Stevenson thought "My God,
the President is describing himself! JFK gets his notion of who
he is from these books, or he might have already had a vision
of himself as a Playboy President and when he came in contact
with Fleming the stories crystallized his image. Either way, in his
mind, James Bond and Jack Kennedy are one-in-the-same. He's
the most powerful man in the world, giving him freedom to try
and live out his fantasies. But fantasies are just that. Try and make
them come to life."

"Take it with you. Read it. Tell me what you think."

They had not spoken since, either in person or on the phone,
but Stevenson had read the book while waiting at the airport for his
shuttle. What he encountered horrified him even as it had earlier
enthralled the President. Here was an entirely amoral saga about a
nasty sadist, not only willing, but eager to inflict death and before
death, considerable pain on his enemies. These included many of
the women he bedded. Bond apparently took a perverse pleasure
in sensing a lover was actually an agent for the other side. His joy
in the sex derived from knowledge that when she afterwards tried
to murder him, he'd turn the tables, watch her die slowly, savoring
every moment. Here was a man who had become an agent not out
of duty to crown and country, rather to exploit the cruel power a
license to kill allowed him. And, lately, Stevenson thought, Mr.
Kiss Kiss, Bang Bang had replaced straight-shooting Lassiter as

our new American hero.

"Oh, I've been meaning to read that!" Stevenson had been yanked out of his cerebral reverie to realize one of the stewardesses stood by his side. Pert and pretty in a fresh new uniform, the girl embodied the notion of her profession as presented in TV advertisements: 'Come fly with me!' a blonde sky-girl suggestively beckoned to viewers.

"You look too sweet," Stevenson mumbled, knowing she had no idea who he was, "to indulge in such trash."

"Oh, I don't know," she winked. "I like to be a little daring, at least when I'm at home reading," she giggled.

He felt charmed by her, charmed and frightened. Doubtless, she'd go to see that movie when it came out. She and millions like her. And, as movies always do to the masses, the film of *Dr. No* would condition her and others in the audience to think that operating as a reckless airborne cowboy is acceptable.

"Here, you're welcome to this copy." He handed her the book. Might as well save her thirty-five cents. What would she say if he told her this was the very copy our sexy young President had read? Doubtless she voted for him, whatever her political allegiances, if she actually had any, because JFK rated as cool!

PRESIDENT KENNEDY DECIDED TO go ahead on the 17th of April 1961. The invasion became known as the *Bay of Pigs* and the disaster caused an angry President Kennedy to call off all further assassination attempts on Castro's life. His brother, Attorney General Robert Kennedy, publicly blamed the CIA for the failure and funds dried up affecting Dave Riley and hundreds of operatives like him.

But, clandestine operations against communist Cuba continued for many years. With an unbelievable 638 recorded attempts on the Cuban dictator's life, Fidel Castro talked of his invincibility in 1967, saying: "If surviving assassination attempts were an Olympic event, I would win a gold medal."

SEVEN

D AVE'S DREAM OF BEING the next Sinatra never faded. He approached Mob-owned record companies and became embroiled with 'the boys.' In the fall of 1961, he met DJ Joey Green at WFUN, where the station's Music Director Jim Timmons suggested Joey play Riley's first song.

By October, Dave had started a relationship with Julie, a secretary at the station. A pretty girl with a perfect figure and long blonde hair, in her early 20s, she had begun working there in the spring of '61. Chuck Berry was forever blasting out *Sweet Little Sixteen* and Joey couldn't help thinking that Julie looked hardly any older than that, with her smooth complexion and rosy cheeks.

Joey was all business at WFUN as a rock jock. He didn't pay that much attention to the women who worked there, but he certainly did a double take when Julie arrived. Joey's first interaction was opened with a cheesy remark—not something he was proud of later, having an aversion to anything bordering on the cliché. He was sorting through some discs when Julie came in with a wide smile on her face.

They said hello and then Joey blurted, "My, you're the prettiest girl I've had in here in ages." Julie laughed, thanked him and he welcomed her to the company, showing her important landmarks like the coffee and cigarette machines that were situated way down the tiled corridor in the austere building. Joey felt like hitting himself in the mouth for his dumb comment, but after the ice was broken they became firm friends.

Dave generally kept girls around for sex or a place to crash, but with Julie there was more going on for the wannabe singer. Dave soon became a permanent fixture at the station. Julie was taken with Dave. Her big blue eyes would light up whenever he sauntered in, often half an hour late, to meet her after work. She reminded Joey of a love-struck teenager—long eyelashes and laughter—but she wasn't a dumb girl, far from it.

Before Joey left WFUN for WGBS and Channel 10 in February, 1962, he often saw the two of them, Dave sitting on the edge of Julie's desk in the front lobby usually involved in serious talk over some papers. Often Lenny and James would accompany Dave and they, too, joined the talks. There was something more going on and Joey couldn't figure it out.

THE CUBANS IN FLORIDA, Joey came to understand after moving to Miami in the spring of '60, were ecstatic about taking Castro down. During his show breaks, from the side windows of the radio studios of WAME in a large Biscayne Boulevard office building, Joey noticed several groups, most numbering around ten, openly plotting an invasion to take their homeland back. The following summer the Cubans provided a major news source.

and reporters eagerly interviewed the self-styled spokesmen.

On any given day, one might hear: "Shortly, a secret brigade, Freedom Forever! We will launch an attack."

Everyone waited, fascinated, but nothing happened. Reeling like little boys who cried wolf, journalists soon ceased reporting on all such predictions. But Miami's anti-Castro Cuban militants were not, as some observers guessed, playing mind-games with the press. They did truly intend to invade. Reporters failed at first to realize that any small group was not a splinter off some larger operation, but rather a self-contained unit. When somebody finally took count, everyone realized such organizations numbered nearly 50, most with membership ranging from five to 20 volunteers. That old adage about too-many-chefs-too-few-cooks completely applied here. Not only did they fail to unite, some groups expressed open hostility toward others. The leaders proved to be egomaniacs viewing counterparts as competitors. Soon angry statements from some patriot cells would be directed at neighbors instead of at Castro. Clearly, they had trouble organizing enough to simply agree on a single leader.

Unity would occur only if someone from the outside came in to take command, a non-Cuban American who understood that these potential warriors could legally perform what the U.S. government wanted to accomplish but was restricted from, even attempting, due to international laws. A military man might have been perfect, though this would have edged too close to illegality. Leadership had to be accomplished via some invisible man, hailing from an agency in Washington, D.C.. Fortunately, at least for those who favored invasion, such an agency existed. It was called the CIA and circumstances allowed Joey to become aware of goings-on in the Cuban American community more than most other reporters.

Around the same time, Green had begun dating the attractive Cuban woman with a Mona-Lisa-like smile, Marisa. Once Green gained her trust, she felt comfortable enough to admit her connections to a group which secretly flew B-26 raids, dropping bombs and leaflets over Cuba. When Joey pressed her as to the identity of her organization, as well as who supplied their planes and ammunition, Marisa sighed that perhaps, when the time was right, she'd tell him. Her admission flabbergasted Joey. This elegant woman lived a double life, not unlike one of the Bond girls in an Ian Fleming story. Marisa did tell Joey that, if contacted by superiors, she must leave immediately, heading off to the Tamiami Airport or some landing strip at a place she wasn't yet free to divulge. Once there, Marisa would hop in a plane, fly down to her homeland, there raining havoc on a designated target below.

At first Joey, wasn't sure he believed her. He'd met some whacky women in Miami, many who told bizarre stories that simply didn't ring true. There was even a group of girls claiming President Kennedy was secretly flying into Miami for sex with them. Still, sudden calls did reach Marisa at odd hours, at clubs where no one could have known Joey and she had slipped off to. Joey would suggest an out of the way spot for dinner. Halfway through, the owner would hurry over, "A call for the lovely lady."

Marisa always insisted they take two cars so she could drive off without having to worry about how Joey would get home. As their relationship grew more serious, Joey began to buy Marisa's story. She decided that if she ever again got the call, always a brief-warning sort of thing, while they were together, Joey could, if he wished, accompany her. That both excited and terrified him. Joey didn't know if he'd go or not. Then it occurred that if all this were true, it would make an incredible news piece that could position him in the forefront of local broadcast journalists, so he said sure. By this time, he'd moved from WAME to WFUN. Joey believed this might be the sort of scoop the station manager, Bud Connor, could go for. However, the timing wasn't right. Whenever he and Marisa were out on a date, such a call failed to come.

Several times, while Joey performed his D.J. night shift, she'd stop by. One night Joey answered the phone to a cold male voice who urgently asked for Marisa. "It's a go right now," she said, unable to stick around long. Frustrated, Joey had to remain in the studio, methodically completing his shift.

One weekend, as they were deciding whether to head for the beach or down to the Keys, this beautiful Cuban suggested they instead drive into the Everglades. At first Joey failed to grasp her deeper meaning, thinking they were either off on a search for intriguing wildlife. As they proceeded along a barely visible trail through foliage so thick it appeared black rather than green, Joey realized that this was the first time they'd gone anywhere in a single car. The truth finally dawned on him when Marisa slowed to a halt at an unexpected guard station. The small outpost was manned by three scruffy fellows, each brandishing a large hand-gun in a holster by his side.

"Hello, Marisa," the trio's leader called out as he stepped from the small white shack.

"Buenos dias, Jonesy,"

Joey's companion answered with a smile. "I hoped to show my companion what we do here."

"Any amigo of yours," the man sweetly sighed, "is ours as well." He cast his dark eyes on Joey, who progressively felt less comfortable. The large fellow, with unruly hair that resembled a crop of thin carrots stretching toward the sky, gave off a horrid odor that reminded Joey of fish. How bizarre that classy Marisa would even know such a rough type.

"I'd best call in all the same," one of the back-up men, who spoke with a Southern drawl and appeared somewhat younger than the leader, suggested. He wore a beat up air-force sweatshirt and sported redneck sideburns.

"You do that, Hank," the one Marisa had referred to as Jonesy called over his shoulder, vaguely annoyed.

"Getting on each other's nerves?" asked Marisa.

The third man, older than the others, stepped forward. "Don't say that," he laughed. "We've come to think of each other as brothers."

The large man rolled his eyes. "Like Sartre said, 'Hell is other people.'"

Joey was amazed to hear a French philosopher quoted here, in the Glades, by such a person.

"Up-the-phone and inform them it's okay to escort Joey onto the property." Marisa said as she waved her thanks. She pulled ahead, past a long stretch of barbed wire fence, this carefully concealed in the twisted overgrowth. As they drove deeper into the swamp, Joey spotted several groups of young Cubans in para-military fatigues, heatedly training under the auspices of similarly attired Anglos. Marisa swerved her car off the trail and onto a gravel stretch, so they could watch experts instructing the Cubans in martial arts, the handling of weapons, and a guerilla tactic in which men silently moved up behind an enemy to slit his throat.

"Hello, Marisa," a tense-looking instructor called out. He announced a five-minute break, then sloshed through putrid water and over wild ferns, approaching the car.

"Haven't seen you out here in a while—Hi, I'm George."

"George...?" Joey asked while suffering under the man's relentlessly hard grip.

"Just, George," Marisa explained. "I'm trying to convince Joey to become one of us," she confided.

"Welcome, Joey, to Operation Vaquero."

Vaquero? Joey thought. Isn't that Spanish for cowboy? Only then did he notice that, traditional military outfit aside, this George fellow wore cowboy boots.

"If you think it's alright, I'll show Joey around."

"Fine. Let me say so long first. I'll be moving my group to either Guatemala or Nicaragua in three days." George smiled, waved, and rejoined his men. Marisa drove on, passing flat fields that cut into the swamp, then across gravel Joey guessed served as take-off and landing points. Joey had entered an alternate little kingdom on the edge of the greater world everyone back in Miami shared. No one made a serious attempt to conceal this place, yet few, if any, in the nearby city knew of its existence. Nor did they care. The media, Joey's own station included, remained blithe about whatever went on in the Glades. If radio, TV, and the newspapers failed to report it, so far as the public at large was concerned, none of this existed.

"Army or Marines?" Joey asked, indicating George with a backward shift of his head.

"Neither. CIA."

Part of him, Joey Green, an all-American boy who still wanted to believe that his country didn't do things in an underhanded or secretive way wanted to leap out, hurry back to where he'd come from, forget what he'd seen. Then Marisa turned to him, offering her irresistible smile. And then his other side, the element that often led him into adventures, if none so potentially dangerous as this, breathed in him deeply.

The following day he broached the subject of a possible story with FUN's news director, the station now relocated from the Beach to the mainland where a more powerful broadcast wattage-system doubled the audience. "Oh!" the manager said, "I don't want to touch that." Hours later and unable to put what he'd seen out of mind, Joey decided to go over the man's head and approach Bud. When Joey mentioned he had stumbled on an exciting and possibly important story, and that WFUN could break the news, Bud's eyes lit up. When Joey explained further, his boss visibly winced.

"No can do," he muttered.

"May I ask why?"

Bud locked eyes with Joey. All at once, the younger man felt naive, melting under a knowing gaze that suggested what the boss was about to explain ought not have to be said.

"Joey, listen to me. There are only two subjects we don't get into. The current Cuban crisis and the Mob."

"Bud, I featured a story about Bobby Kennedy's big new crusade on organized crime just this afternoon."

"No problem. It'll also be on network news. There's a difference between re-stating what's on-air, taking place in the national arena and stirring up things locally."

"And the Glades? Why a black-op there...?"

"Patriotism. Castro's a menace to our way of life. In due time, these guys are going to go down to Cuba and take him out. That'll be good for America."

"No one wants to print stuff which might give Fidel any advance word."

"So, we're censored?"

"No one's said a word from Washington. No one will."

"A gentleman's agreement."

"I hate to admit it, but...yeah."

"How about our promise to tell the truth...?"

"That, I consider our second greatest responsibility."

"And our first?" Joey asked.

"Survival as a country."

Those words resonated through Joey's mind. This was virtually what Dave had said several months earlier. Weird that two people as different as Bud Connor and Dave Riley might come to the same conclusion on anything, Green thought.

A FEW DAYS BEFORE leaving his DJ job at WFUN for all news station WGBS, Green walked out of the studio to pick up a delivery from reception and found Julie at her desk with Dave beside her. They were whispering about something and when she spotted the DJ she elbowed Dave to be quiet.

"Hi Joey..." she said quickly, slipping a sheet of paper under a file on her desk. "How're you today?"

"Um...OK thanks. Is that the package for me?"

"Hey, Green." chipped in Dave. "Can you drop me at the airport later?"

"Hey, he isn't your personal taxi," joked Julie, nudging a

grinning Dave and passing Joey the small package.

"No problem, I'll be going that way anyhow," Joey said and went towards the station manager's office. Before he headed down the hallway he glanced at the pair and there they were again, deep in hushed conversation.

Weird, Joey thought and then recalled that one night Dave came into the station when Joey had just finished work at Midnight and asked for a ride to Julie's place. To Joe's surprise, it turned out to be situated in one of the plushest apartment blocks in North Miami, an affluent area, filled with trendy bars and clubs and awash with flashy rich kids in expensive clothes and even more expensive cars. How can Julie afford that on a secretary's salary, he thought as he dropped Dave off, said goodbye and drove on home. And then there were the instances Green found her quickly cramming a note into her bag or her drawer when he walked by her desk. Was it possible that, being a right-wing, pro-American patriot, something she had in common with Riley, that Julie was working with Dave?

Green's curiosity was triggered by all this, but being friends, particularly with Julie, Joey didn't want to appear nosey by asking questions. He wasn't close enough to either of them on a personal level to pry. But Dave's obsession with carrying a pistol wherever he went and his apparent jumpiness at times did plant questions in Green's mind.

IN LATE MARCH 1962, the CIA told Riley about a more complicated and important mission he was to front scheduled for Friday, April 13. Twenty-eight missions to Cuba and to that date and not once was David Riley questioned by Castro's police, the

Army or everyday middle class civilians who looked and acted like him. With each success his ego grew exponentially. He believed he was invincible—feeling the pulse as if he was the number one Island spy, ready for any assignment. His fine-tuned Cuban Spanish and his Cuban disguise at the ready and his alter-ego, David Montez, was about to make another grand entrance on board a Cuban-bound Cessna 172 at Tamiami airport.

—Little did Dave know about the furor that was about to erupt.

EIGHT

"JEEZ," SAID LENNY, FROM behind Riley, prodding him in the shoulder blade. He, Dave and James were walking across a tarmac area of Tamiami Airport, directly south of Miami International. At any one time there were hundreds of small passenger planes being parked and maintained there and the place was big enough—and security lax enough—that a CIA operation of say 20 or 30 small Beech Crafts, Cessnas and Piper Apaches wouldn't be noticed amongst all the other planes that flew to and from the compound.

"What?" barked Dave, looking sharp in his newly re-grown handlebar moustache and aviator sunglasses which shaded his eyes from the bright spring glare.

"This place is swarming with pilots today," answered Lenny, pointing in front of him. "Look at all those guys up ahead." He motioned towards a bunch of men in varied casual attire, who were either standing in groups or milling around, chatting and laughing, not too far from the runway and their private aircrafts parked nearby. Pilots, no doubt, waiting for their pre-booked clients to turn up, people wanting flying lessons or eager day-trippers and tourists with cameras looped around their necks expecting to be flown over the Everglades or Miami and the Keys.

"We're in an airport. Pilots work in airports. What did you expect?" Dave stopped walking towards one of the one-story airport buildings, swiped his sunglasses off and squinted at Lenny.

"So, what's the score again?" asked Lenny, who was wearing a khaki t-shirt and matching Bermuda shorts and had also recently grown a bushy moustache.

"Like I said earlier, man…we've got a plane booked for a tour around the Everglades," cut in James, who was to be the pilot for the mission. "Then we go on a slight detour—to Cuba."

"Easy." smiled Dave, "Everyone's too busy with their own thing here to ask us anything, anyway, so be cool." He wiped his shades on the bottom of his linen shirt, put them back on and carried on moving, whistling as he went.

"But, I am cool." Lenny held his hands out, trotting quickly behind Dave, who took no notice. "See, I'm cool. Cool as a cucumber in actual fact."

"OK, OK, I think I got it, Len," said Dave.

James made a loud tutting sound. He was used to his friends' inane discussions and was eager to get up into the sky. It was the only place he felt he belonged. There was nothing he loved more than flying. He shoved his hands in his Levi pockets and strode ahead into one of the low white prefabricated aluminum buildings that stood at Tamiami Airport. Dave and Lenny waited for him to come out with the keys to the Cessna 172 the Feds had previously booked for them under a false company and pilot's name. The young guy behind the desk hadn't even asked for ID or so much as glanced up at James. He was too busy admiring a photo of Playmate of the Month, Roberta Lane, in Playboy's April '62 edition.

"Did you tell the guy at the desk the trip was for my birthday?" Lenny smiled at James. He and his two friends were a tight team and he liked to imagine that they never made mistakes but Lenny was a perfectionist and always had to ensure their stories were poker straight which the other two found mildly amusing.

"What? Oh, yeah, you're 30th," smirked James.

"You saying I look 30?" Lenny put his hands on his hips.

James held his stubbly chin and scrutinized his friend, his light green eyes squinting into slits. "Sure. You could pass for 30."

"But I'm 28...," complained Lenny.

"Jeez, it doesn't matter whether you said the plane was for a visit to Santa Claus in his... his...fucking little gingerbread cottage in the North Pole—or wherever the sucker lives. No one gives a shit here. Just get on the fucking plane will you?" Dave walked towards the Cessna with his two accomplices following on his tail.

"Did anyone bring any sodas?" asked Lenny. His friends ignored him and James opened the small aluminum doors of the Cessna to climb on board. "I'm thirsty," continued Lenny.

James waited for the plane in front of him to take off and he rolled the craft down the runway and took to the air while Lenny and Dave cheered. For a moment his friends didn't speak, concentrating on the exhilarating upward movement of the plane and then as it went in a southerly direction, slicing across the blue sky and following the edges of the Keys. Dave sat next to James in the passenger seat and Lenny was in the back, staring down at the ground below as it grew more and more distant.

"I wish I'd brought a soda," whispered Lenny in a wistful tone.

Dave's eyes rolled upwards. "You'll have to wait 'til we get there."

While Lenny fell into a snooze in the back, sending gentle snores into the air, James and Dave carried on in quiet anticipation.

"How long to Cuba now?" asked Dave, suddenly cutting through an unusual episode of peace.

"Roughly an hour," said James, the plane's nose still pointing southeast, in order to avoid flying over Havana itself.

"We're halfway then. Cool," nodded Dave.

"Huh?" A mumble came from the back seat.

"Not far, Lenny," said Dave loudly.

"Once we're there where's our first mark?" asked Lenny, having woken from his nap and was now yawning.

Dave turned in his seat slightly and addressed his friends. "OK, now I need you to listen to me carefully, guys. This is important. First we get to a town some place east, 40 miles from the capital..."

"Where we staying?" interrupted James.

"The Feds got us some kind of boarding house or big hotel or something they said. I have to call them when we get to the base outside Havana for the details. Then someone will come pick us up," explained Dave.

"So they should," said James. "Bound to be a special car..."

"Yeah, we're special agents now—their top guys," agreed Lenny. "Huh Dave?"

"Sure as shit we are, buddy!" Dave and Lenny slapped palms and whooped.

"We gotta find this General guy—General Juan Franco Hernandez or some dumb name. Anyhow, Monday afternoon he's holding a meeting with some of Castro's goons in some old Army building out in the sticks. The Feds will give us the time and place and we report back when we've seen him. Easy! Sunday night we head South, when we get orders."

Part of the CIA's agenda was to give at least two groups of operatives or case workers some of the exact same orders—they would set up a time and a place for a target to be spotted and if each group of operatives reported back with a matching time, location and story, the Feds knew they could be trusted to carry out further covert missions or assignments. It was a tireless directive that was often viewed as time-wasting by many who worked for the organization, although Dave, James and Lenny, being on the lowest rung of the hierarchical ladder, had no idea of such contrived wild goose chases. They just dutifully followed orders that seemed meaningless to them. Their gathered information was pieced together back in Miami by higher-ups they had never met.

"We get our own transport?" asked Lenny.

"They'll give us whatever we want," shrugged Dave.

"Easy as shit," nodded James.

"Yup," said Dave. "Like I said."

There were a few moments of thought as each man considered the mission ahead and what was involved—their pride in fighting for the good of their country at the forefront of their minds, without a doubt.

"I been thinking a lot recently…" began Lenny.

"Well done," butted in James.

"I been thinking. I reckon once they've asked us to bump off Castro and his goons, next time they'll most likely send us to spy on the Soviets," said Lenny. "Seems the most likely place when you think about it. We'll get a crack at all those KGB commie bastards. Bam!" Lenny cocked a pretend pistol in the air and let it fire.

"Could be…could be," thought James, aloud, imagining the scene. "We'll be all-American heroes. Then we'll wipe out all the commie's in the world and come back home to a hero's welcome. Our names will be in all the newspapers and we'll be on TV!"

"My brothers would blow a fucking gasket if they saw that," laughed Dave, fired up with intense enthusiasm.

"They'll be lining the streets to welcome us!" Lenny leaned in from the back and slapped James' seat, sending him forward.

"Hey, easy…" James said.

"We'll get any chick we want!" added Lenny. "The Feds'll buy us houses on the beach! We'll get in any club we want—VIP style!"

"Hey, we're the Firm's top guys now. Remember, we go where we want, we do what we want, and we tell them when to jump," Dave placed his hands behind his head and smiled. "The Firm depends on top guys like us—like I told you."

"You reckon, Dave?"

"I don't just reckon, Lenny. I friggin' know it."

"Hey, man, just look at the three of us now—we ain't no street punks no more!" laughed James, clapping his hands and looking at his friends. "We got money, we got women, we got a plane, we got…"

"I'll tell you what you got. You gotta look where you're going, that's what you got," Dave said as the Cessna dipped toward the edge of the Caribbean below.

"Sorry, man," said James, his eyes darting ahead.

"Dave?" asked Lenny.

"Yep?"

"But there's something else I've been thinking about a lot recently as well."

"Fucking hell, Lenny. Don't wear your brain out all at once," said James. "You might need it later."

"Shut up, James, you dumb prick," snapped Lenny.

"What, Len?" asked Dave, laughing loudly, his head thrown back.

"What'll we get when we've wiped out the commies? Will we get a medal? I'd like that."

"Don't doubt it, Lenny," said Dave.

The three men whooped again, hyped up with adrenalin and anticipation for their futures.

"All their top guys like us get shit-loads of medals. The Feds'll be lining up to throw a whole pile of the things at us."

The trio carried on laughing and talking while staring out of the plane's windows, as they said goodbye to the last vestiges of U.S. land that disappeared into the far off distance and way behind into the horizon.

"Cuba, here we come!" yelled James, minutes later. "Yeehah!"

"Yeehah!" chimed in the other two.

Twelve miles from the shores of Cuba, the guys were now aware that they were entering enemy territory and if deemed to be violating Cuban airspace, they could be in big trouble. Although they knew that they had to be on the lookout for other aircraft, for a time, it seemed that they were the only ones in the sky. James kept his gaze in the direction of the Cuban coast which wouldn't be too far ahead now.

"Hey, look!" said James, all of a sudden alarmed.

"Huh," replied Dave, sitting up straight and peering out of the front window. "Shit. It's another plane."

"Do you reckon they've seen us?" asked Lenny.

"Hey, I hope not," said Dave.

"Is it a fighter jet?" asked Lenny.

"Not sure, but it don't look too friendly to me that's for sure." Dave shook his head.

"How does a plane look friendly anyhow?" asked James, his eyes rolling to heaven.

"I don't know." murmured Dave. "How come you expect me to know everything?"

"He's right. It doesn't look friendly," agreed Lenny.

The three men watched as the other craft—light grey in color, with a sharply pointed nose, flew levelly for a few minutes, picked up at full speed, sending shafts of smoke across the atmosphere, and then, at last it was gone.

"Nope, they didn't see us," said Lenny, relieved.

Their plane had entered Cuban airspace in approximately two hours. The trio was blissfully unaware, thanks to the lack of information fed to them by the CIA, that one of the many MIG jets, known to be circling this island country, leased or given to Castro's revolutionary government by the Soviet Union, might mistake them for a U.S. Air Force craft and shoot them out of the sky.

The Feds didn't stress the extreme danger they were putting their operatives in on these flights to Cuba. Like a last meal in a prison before an execution, they were treated well—while they lived. Crucial details were kept from their operatives. Unlike a doctor giving a patient the scientific chances of recovery for an operation, the CIA thought revealing that would drastically cut the numbers of volunteers from which they choose. Ground forces might well assume that the Cessna had been launched as the tip of yet another wave of American Imperialism, *Bay of Pigs* style, full of anti-Fidel Cubans. Dave and his two friends had no idea that they were taking that kind of a chance with their lives that day. True the Agency valued their loyalty and service, but not to the extent that they weren't expendable for the benefit of all the millions of Americans. Degenerates like Riley and his little gang were necessary commodities to the CIA. Big decisions like that were made at the CIA desks in Miami or the world headquarters in Langley, Virgina, just across the Potomac River from Washington D.C..

After the *Bay of Pigs*, America, now disgraced in the world's eyes, desperately hoped to find some way to kick-start its status as a superpower. And as a precaution, Fidel's forces might easily have shot the plane down, just like the U.S. might have any unidentified plane that came roaring up toward Florida from the South. The trio had so far escaped death, but little did they know that they were about to find themselves on gravely dangerous territory even after a safe landing.

James flew over one of the island's sprawling beaches and then spotted sweeping green hills looming against the bright sky.

"We're here!" yelped Lenny and looked at Dave's profile.

"Cool," said Dave, stretching.

"Not far now, guys" said James, scanning the rough terrain underneath. He spotted a dirt road below and smiled. He knew it must lead directly to the military base, where he had been ordered to land.

Unlike U.S. bases, Cuban ones were set up in makeshift style and, luckily for James and his cronies, security was always slack in such places. Soldiers wouldn't think it abnormal for a small plane to land there—the reason the CIA used Pipers and Cessnas, as bigger crafts were far more likely to have been shot down. The little planes could more easily skirt Cuban radar. The whole island was an armed camp, expecting an invasion, and there were plane spotters everywhere. The base below was perfect for the mission. The men couldn't possibly have gotten through the island's Jose Marti Airport without being stopped and having to show papers to awaiting security guards.

James circled twice, checking his controls, peering down at a deserted compound. Half a dozen rusty tin buildings circled a larger, older wood-frame structure which was surrounded by dusty grey sand and patches of grass. An arid landing strip stretched toward the West, a primitive narrow clearing slashed into a deep tangle of weeds, with shoulder-high cane and an encroaching jungle in the near distance.

"Man this place is crazy," whistled James.

"It ain't Miami International Airport. That's for sure," agreed Lenny. "It's like the back of beyond."

"This is real old Cuban territory," said Dave. "What did you expect—naked chicks in strip joints with neon lights?"

"I wish," sighed Lenny.

Most of rural Cuba was to the East of the island's capital, where Castro started his rebel fight in the Sierra Maestra Mountains, even deeper into the country, about 900 miles East of Havana and very close to the American Naval Base, Guantanamo, held by the U.S. since the Spanish American War in 1898 and never challenged by Castro.

Now descending toward the dusty strip, "Here we go! Ready for landing!" shouted James. Minutes later, they met the ground with a gentle bump, careered forward a few yards and came to a juddering halt.

"Nice going, James," said Dave.

James glanced to his left, through the window and squinted in the harsh sunlight. Dave pointed at the wooden barn-like building. "I guess we should go in that direction," he said and got out of his seat. "The Feds'll be waiting for us to make contact. Don't wanna keep the guys waiting."

What he and the others hadn't noticed were the group of men with Czech-made VZ53 semi-automatic machine guns clutched in their hands. Having watched the plane circle and land they were now stealthily scaling around the tail of the plane, ready to make their presence known.

"Come on out with your hands in the air," A Cuban soldier ordered in broken English and pointed his machine gun at the windscreen of the plane, "Or we will shoot. Do you understand?"

"Oh shit..." Dave shrieked as he saw the hate-fueled faces of a dozen other young Cubans, all sporting Fidel-like beards, uniformed in drab olive fatigues, poised to fire at the slightest provocation. Dave, Lenny and James were now deathly quiet and still, the bravado they had shared on the plane had now fizzled out.

"What the hell is this?" Dave whispered to James, highly offended. "I thought they'd greet us with Cuban cigars and ice cold beers—but this?"

"Step down from the plane slowly," one bearded Cuban, obviously the squad commander, barked out orders while beckoning for them to alight from the craft, his other arm cradling a weapon.

Dave rose to disembark first. Summing up his courage, he pushed the plane's doors aside and crawled out, hands held high. He glanced back at James, who was following behind, visibly shaking with fear, his hands also waving above his head.

"What are they going to do to us?" James whispered, almost weeping.

"I don't know," Dave hissed. "We'll find out soon enough, I'm sure."

Lenny then dropped down from the plane with a loud thud, landing awkwardly on hard dirt. Before he could regain his balance a Cuban shoved his submachine gun in his chest.

Lenny's hands shot upwards. "Please don't shoot me!" he cried and stumbled into line with his two buddies.

"Make any moves and we will kill you," the squad leader insisted. A considerable arsenal of weapons remained trained on the three as the Cubans roughly escorted them to G-2, the office of Castro's secret police, in the central wood-plank construction of the crude outpost. The imposing Cuban who had shouted out orders now accosted and accused all three, insisting they must be agents from the CIA, FBI, American Immigration or any other similar outfit he cared to name. Dave, Lenny and James at once began to deny all, pleading innocence and ignorance in turn while on their way to the rustic headquarters. Once inside the building, they were shoved into a small dark room, lit only by a single hanging bulb.

Standing with sub-machine guns pointed at their foreheads by a line-up of very angry-looking Cuban soldiers the trio closed their eyes and prayed for it to be over quickly. They had heard stories about what happened to Americans trespassing on enemy soil and these guys had made it obvious that they weren't keen on listening.

Dave knew full well that if it was found out that they were working for the CIA, he and his buddies would be killed as soon as they could blink. They had to make these army goons believe that they were simply three irresponsible young clowns out on a joyride. Dave's brain ticked over. He had to say something quick, but what? The commander stepped forward and pushed an AK-47 into Dave's throat. Hot tears welled in Riley's eyes.

The leader then growled, "You have four seconds to tell me who you are or I will kill you. One, two, three..."

NINE

THE COMMANDER'S SEMI-AUTOMATIC machine gun dug deeper into Dave's windpipe. Any minute now he feared that his head was going to be parting company with the rest of his anatomy and he shook with terror. He could smell the stale body odor that filled the air in the windowless wooden shack and see the pockmarks on the Commander's sweat-drenched face, now that he was in such close proximity. Dave's mind was racing, going back and forth over his CIA training. What should he say? He had to make them believe that he was David Montez, a Cuban citizen like them. However, he hadn't bargained on being caught and interrogated at the Army base. He knew that he had to try and stay calm and hope that Lenny and James kept their mouths shut until he had talked them out of this situation. Although they had been trained to speak Cuban Spanish too they weren't as fluent as Riley and he wasn't convinced that they could pull off being credible Cubans. Dave was the talent in this set up, but with a deadly weapon digging in his throat he was having trouble thinking straight. He had to come up with an answer fast only when he opened his mouth to speak in

Spanish, as David Montez, someone got there before him, cutting him off.

"This is your last chance to tell me who you are…I have nearly finished counting…" The Cuban leader then yelled, making Dave and his buddies jump, "Four!"

But Dave's deep shock was about to worsen.

"Please, please help me!" gabbled James at the top of his voice, springing forward from the back wall of the gloomy room. "I'm an American citizen…a pilot. These two guys booked me from Tamiami Airport, said they wanted a trip over Florida Keys… and…and," he stammered with the flats of his hands held up in front of him as if to shield himself from any bullets that might soon come his way.

"Get back against the wall!" yelled the Commander. James did as he was ordered but carried on with his speech, "You have to believe me. I don't know these two guys…they put a gun to my head, they made me fly here!"

Mortified that James had not only given them up as Americans, but that he was lying through his teeth, Dave shook his head vigorously, trying to gain his friend's attention, but James was too busy addressing the Commander, who now glanced at James and then at Dave and then back again. There was deep suspicion in his dark eyes. Something wasn't adding up here. This was the first time that the men had shown any dissension between them. James' sudden hysteria only added to his disbelief.

"I need you to help me get back to Miami!" James pleaded with the Commander. "This has nothing to do with me!"

"You slimy bastard," seethed Dave, stepping forward to grab James, but the Kalashnikov pointed at him by the Commander made him move back against the wall.

Dave threw a look of pure hatred at James, silently warning him to shut up or else. What was Eaton up to? He couldn't believe that his own friend of five years would sell him out like that.

One of the main reasons the trio had been trained to speak Spanish beforehand was to fool interrogators if they so happened to be caught, which was considered an unlikely scenario, so the CIA had maintained during the training program. The CIA drummed it into their new operatives that they were not supposed to say they were from the U.S. as that would cause huge diplomatic trouble of catastrophic proportions—and the Feds had had enough accusations leveled at them lately. And now James was about to land the three of them in big trouble and no doubt gain them a death sentence in the bargain. From that moment on James Eaton was worse than pond scum to Riley.

"You, shut the fuck up," Dave whispered through gritted teeth, the sweat on his forehead from the suffocating heat seeping into his eyes, making them sting. There was no way he could get away with the whole Cuban David Montez plan now. He and Lenny were going to have to get themselves out of this one without James.

But James was ignoring Dave and had no intention of shutting up, not if his neck was on the line. He never promised the CIA that he would give up his life for them. He was no puppet. Eaton's sense of patriotism was obviously not quite as strong as Dave and Lenny's, who also tried whispering for him to keep quiet, but with James' cries and the shouting of the guards the noise in the Army hut was radiant.

James ignored both of his friends and continued, "I'm not FBI or CIA…I mean, c'mon, do I look like CIA?" He let out a weird strangled laugh. "I'm just a pilot and I want to go home…these two guys kidnapped me at gunpoint! They told me to find a place to land outside Havana. It's all a stupid mistake!"

The Commander put up his hand as if to say "enough" and squinted at the trio, all in ridiculous, almost matching, cowboy boots and practically blubbering like newborn babies. They looked really stupid all right, but he couldn't be sure if he was indeed witnessing a kidnapping or they had been sent to spy by some American organization. There was something that wasn't adding up here and he couldn't work out what it was just yet. He needed time. He certainly didn't believe that this was a simple plane ride that just happened to end in the middle of his own Army camp or that these men hadn't known one another beforehand. The kidnapping story was too idiotic to be true, surely? They sure didn't fit the stereotype brush cut and white bucks Ivy League type agents who were the mainstay of the CIA. But like other Castro followers the Commander had no idea of the CIA's policy of employing ex-felons. The Commander was tiring of the three men and wasn't about to take any chances.

"Do you think I am stupid?" he shouted and aimed his AK-47 at James' head, who let out a piercing scream and put his hands in front of his face as a shield.

The leader's comrades were lined up behind him—a barrage of semi-automatic machine guns pointed at Dave, James and Lenny. The men were just waiting for the chance to release a hail of bullets into the torsos of these whinning American capitalist pigs' bodies. They only needed one word from the Commander. It wouldn't be the first time and it wouldn't be the last either. They saw it as a perk of the job.

"Please, I have nothing to do with them! Help me get back to Miami!" James shouted. "If you just let me go back to the plane, I can fly home and we can all pretend that this never…"

The Commander's face was taken over by a disgusted rage and suddenly he whacked James around the head with his weapon, sending him sprawling to the hard mud of the hut's floor, knocking him out cold. "Shut up you stupid American pigs! I am sick of you fucking people!" He yelled and turned to the soldier by his side and then barked something in his own language. As the three captives were seized by the leader's men, the Commander drew close to Dave and Lenny and growled, "Maybe you all need a few days on your own—to think about the meaning of the truth, huh?" With that he motioned to his men to take them away, where they were dragged to the windowless tin huts that were dotted around the compound, and each man thrown into his own individual dark cell.

For two days, Riley and the others gasped hungrily for air and sweated through their clothes as the mid-afternoon sun turned their shacks into blast furnaces, almost roasting them alive. Once a day a tray of slop was pushed into their rooms by one of the soldiers, their weakening pleas to be released only answered with insults in Spanish and kicks to the head and groins. The men's captors didn't see fit to bring them water with their food, so when the biting thirst began to swell their tongues and drive them towards hallucination and insanity, Dave, Lenny and James resorted to drinking their own urine, soaking up the liquid on their tongues as they wrung droplets out of their saturated trousers. But the terrible thirst could never be quenched and each man begged and cried out for a glass of water. When the mood took them, the guards dragged them separately to the main building for interrogation, barking the same questions at them over and over again until every syllable melded into a never-ending cacophony of meaningless noise.

Dave and Lenny remained resolute in their patriotism and refused to admit to being CIA or part of any organization. But having already been outed as Americans by James, they had no other option but to play dumb and stick to the story that they were simply three bozos out on a joyride. Throughout their interrogations, the two men maintained that they flew to Cuba on a childish dare between buddies, simply to see if they could dodge Cuban radar—and they promised that James' story was nothing but a pile of lies. But the three men's differing tales did nothing but add to the Commander's fury and each day the captives were thrown back in the pitch black tin cells, bruised and bleeding from punches and kicks to the face and body. Lenny had even lost two of his front teeth and Dave squinted out of eyelids that were purple and swollen into pockets of raised flesh. By the end of the second day of interrogations the men had to maintain constant concentration just to stay sane, and just as they began to think that they were never getting out of the situation alive the guards threw the doors of the tin shacks wide open, letting in the harsh daylight that almost blinded the trio.

"Please, let me go!" screamed James whilst he and the others were dragged to an awaiting Army vehicle. "I have nothing to do with this! I was kidnapped! Please!"

"Squealer…" mumbled Dave through the dried blood on his parched lips.

But no one was listening to James' pathetic cries. The Commander had made other, far more important, plans for his prisoners.

"Where are you taking us?" asked James as the fingers of the two guards holding him dug into the flesh of his arms.

Again, he was ignored and in his terror he didn't hear the order that the Commander barked in Spanish, "Take them to El Principe," he instructed his lackeys after receiving a reply to his earlier call to headquarters in Havana. His men nodded, herding the three hand-cuffed captives away from the huts and forced them under a tarpaulin that covered the rear of a large old military truck.

"Where are they taking us?" James repeated, looking at Dave and Lenny in the near-darkness of the dank-smelling truck.

Dave had heard and understood the Commander's order and knew what was in store. His heart began to race. He was briefed about El Principe, the most notorious prison in the western hemisphere. Dave had heard enough horror stories about what happened to people who got thrown in there and the CIA had warned him not to end up in a Cuban jail, especially El Principe. Dave felt sick, but somehow the sight of James' tear-streaked face made him sicker.

"They're taking us to El Principe, asshole," Dave mumbled as he felt the vehicle's engine charge up and heard muffled Spanish coming from the front.

"El Principe?" James repeated, hunched up and holding onto his knees. "Well, that doesn't sound so bad." Then, anxiously, "Does it?"

Lenny sat as upright as he could in the now moving truck, rubbed at a deep gash on his forehead and peered hopefully at

Dave. "It can't be any worse than what we've just been through, surely? Huh, Dave?"

Dave didn't have the guts to give his friend a straight answer or even look him in the eye.

"We're about to find out, Lenny," he whispered.

TEN

———

TAKING DUBIOUS CENTER-STAGE in Havana, a building constructed in 1589 as a Spanish fort, in response to enemy raids on the city's bay, has since served as the harshest prison in the whole of Cuba and casts an eerie shadow across the neighboring region. To be sentenced to a jail term there has sent a shiver of terror down the spine of even the hardest and toughest murderer or serial killer over the centuries. El Castillo del Principe has always been considered a dungeon of the very worst kind—what Dave Riley and others before and since has referred to as a "chamber of horrors."

Hewn from impenetrable rough stone, El Castillo del Principe's high walls can be seen for miles by anyone who glances up at the hill on which it was erected. It provides everyone who looks upon it with a dark and frightening eyesore, in striking contrast with the bustling life below in the attractive historical section of the island's capital, called Ciudad las Columnas.

Up until January 1, 1959, the thousands of men held in the prison were suspected of trying to topple Fulgencia Batista's dictatorial regime. Anyone considered a traitorous revolutionary was rounded up and marched there from enclaves in the city, as well as remote villages right across Cuba. Once inside its imposing walls, captives were thrown in damp, cockroach-infested cells, starved, beaten, tortured and interrogated. And in numerous cases, dragged back out and forced into trucks which carried terrified victims to an isolated area of land for mass execution, usually by a single gun shot to the head. Occasionally these men were granted the so-called dignity of being buried in shallow graves. More often than not though, corpses rotted in the sun-trapped fields in rural areas so that passersby could bear witness to the barbarism going on around them in every corner of their country. It was a stark warning to those with even a hint of rebellion in mind, "Toe the line or you're next."

American style democracy, much less socialism of the type then spreading across the post-WWII political and global landscape, was not to be mentioned or practiced on Cuban soil prior or after the late 50s. It was an abomination to this proud isle. To so much as whisper about any kind of opposing political beliefs to the ones of those in power might earn someone a one-way ticket to El Principe, and no man in his right mind wanted to do anything that might risk that. It was a fate worse than death.

But then El Principe's constituency reversed itself in a single historic day. Batista friendly American political advisors and Mob casino owners deserted by plane after their hedonistic '59 New Year's Eve celebration degenerated into a bloodbath. Fulgencio Batista himself vanished into thin air as his once loyal army threw down weapons and ran away or joined the guerillas. Rebels waved red banners on the streets and wielded pistols. Citizens of

Cuba opened their once closed doors, offering food and wine to the liberators. The political prisoners held inside the prison were released and those who had been guarding them were forced into tiny, blood-stained cells to take their place. But El Principe always had and always would remain a house of horrors. The only difference was that in just 24 hours its constituency had been turned on its head. The conditions inside the huge construction and the harsh treatment meted out to its prisoners still remained the same afterwards. Modern civil and human rights campaigns fell on deaf ears when it came to the treatment of those hidden from sight behind this monstrous building's thick walls.

Once inside you truly became one of the living dead. Falling into the grips of insanity was always a prevalent hazard for anyone held there and medical treatment for prisoners remained non-existent. Medical students with little training were often the only surgeons on hand to perform such operations as tonsillectomies, without any proper facilities or the presence of a senior and fully qualified expert. These men were the student's guinea pigs.

Over many years, El Principe's reign as the most barbaric penal institution in Cuba continued, as did its reputation and stories of appalling human rights atrocities. If those held inside didn't starve to death or become another fatality because of lack of doctor's care or because of electric shock tortures, beatings and poisonings by prison guards, then enforced hard labor or deadly disease, such as tuberculosis, anemia and pneumonia served as a timely epidemic, wiping out Cuba's unwanted or forgotten men. And if death didn't get them, then would self-mutilation, insanity or suicide.

DAVE, JAMES AND LENNY sat hunched and hand-cuffed in the back of the old Soviet Army truck as it drove through thick jungle and untamed rural terrain, bumping over makeshift roads that sent them sprawling to the other side of the vehicle and back again. Three guards squatted in the rear with them on metal benches and the rest of the soldiers were in the front. No one spoke much during the long journey to Havana, but now and again a guard would point his semi-automatic submachine gun at one of the trio if he moved or went to open his mouth to whisper to his friend. The guards' attitude was that these stupid Americans weren't even worth the trouble of being imprisoned. They were an affront to Fidel Castro's proud regime and so what if a stray bullet found its way across the moving vehicle and killed one of them? Cuban bullets were too good for them. But, they had their orders. The men were to be delivered to their destination alive.

The cloying midday heat in the truck sucked almost every ounce of carbon dioxide out of the atmosphere, offering no reprieve from the suffocating sensation that made the captives cough, sweat dripping down their faces and onto their shirts, making long V patterns down the front of the material. The guards shared liter bottles of water, glugging the liquid down greedily and grinning at the three men, while swaying the bottles in front of their dejected faces.

"Thirsty, huh?" said one of the guards, smiling, his tobacco blackened front teeth showing. He kicked out at Dave with a heavy boot, catching him painfully on the shin, asking him once again if he wanted a drink. The bottle rattled in his hand provocatively. But Dave, James and Lenny knew it was all part of the game and ignored the taunts, and carried on staring at the green metal floor of the truck. One wrong move and they knew it could be their last, but if they had been aware of the full horror of what lay ahead at El Principe prison they may well have opted for a quick bullet to the skull.

Soon the rough terrain turned into tight winding streets as they hit the outskirts of Havana and the two-and-a-half ton vehicle squeezed its way down narrow alleyways filled with passersby and random market stalls selling leather or ceramic goods. The city was alive. Crowds of kids milled about, small huddles of old people chatted on steps or in doorways and women in summery clothes shopped. A clock chimed in the distance. A dog barked. A man mended the wheel on his rusty bike at the side of a busy road. But inside the vehicle, the three men sweltered in the intense heat knowing they were drawing closer to their doom and this could be the last time they would be close to the everydayness of the outside world.

They carried on for a while, until the truck came to a halt and the three guards in the back got out and ushered their captives onto the cobbled street, still handcuffed. The lead guard, taller, squarer and wider than the others, peered closely at Dave, Lenny, and James as they stood, backs against the truck, squinting at their new surroundings and a few random locals who had come to stare at the prisoners.

The main guard motioned at a cavernous building at the top of the hill. His arms swept extravagantly out to his sides in a gesture of mock welcome and he bowed his head, looked back up and burst out laughing.

"Here's your new home. You like?"

Dave had seen pictures of El Principe before. He had watched news clips on TV about missing Americans who had been thought to have been thrown into the cells there, without a fair trial, so he knew what to expect. But seeing it for real was vastly different. He was speechless, could hardly breathe. It looked evil, ancient and somewhat gnarled in appearance, as if it had grown and sprouted up and outwards from the ground. It stood like a large monstrous entity that would devour all who went near it. Dave could envision age-old methods of torture—people being laid out on racks, naked prisoners lacerated with cutting implements or burnt with hot electric cables or probes until they screamed for death. His imagination hadn't let him down unfortunately. He shuddered and tears filled his eyes.

When he told Green all about the horrors of El Principe, 2 years later he acted cool, as if nothing fazed him, like he always did. But, Joey could sense the emotion carefully tucked away behind his bravado. Even the biggest and toughest of men would have been shaking in his shoes.

Lenny was staring at Dave, trying to get his attention, as if asking "What now?" but Dave didn't have any answers or any ingenious back-up plans. There was no getting out of this and the CIA sure wasn't coming to save their asses. They didn't send lawyers, government officials or bundles of bribery money in used dollar bills to spring operatives out of stinking foreign hell-holes. Dave knew full well that if he was to get out of this alive he was going to have to get through any kind of torture that was coming his way, keep his story straight and pray for the best. Not that he believed much in all that God baloney, but he thought he would throw in a quick word with the man upstairs anyhow. It couldn't hurt, he reasoned.

As the three men were pushed along by the guards, weapons

rammed into their necks and backs at varying intervals, Dave took a quick glance in James' direction. He had tears running down his bruised face, but this time there were no pleas for freedom. For once, he was silent, dumb-stricken. Dave could understand his fear, but his weakness sickened him.

"This is Cuba's finest prison!" smirked the lead guard, waving his Kalashnikov in the air like a victory flag caught on a breeze. "El Castillo del Principe! People from all over the world come here to stay. Aren't you lucky?" He let out another hoot of laughter at his own caustic wit and his comrades followed suit.

"These big mouth capitalists don't have much to say for a change," sniggered one of the other guards. "But I think they will become more talkative later."

The lead guard motioned for the three men to follow him in the direction of the prison, and with Cubans tight on either side they trudged up the hill towards the doorway of the huge building.

"I can't do this," James whimpered and looked around in a panic, as if trying to find an escape route. "I can't do this."

"Shut up, asshole!" Dave hissed. "Haven't you done enough? Just keep quiet and do as they say or we're dead."

"I don't have to do what you say any more, Riley," whimpered James. "You got me into this. I didn't even want to come."

Dave swung around and glared at James, wishing he could punch him flat out. "I didn't see you complaining when I sprung you out of the Miami Jail. I didn't hear you fucking cry like a big baby when you got on the plane here a few days back, you prick. I didn't see you turn down the money either."

"No talking, stupid American idiots," a guard barked over his shoulder while another hit Dave in the back of the skull with the barrel of his weapon. Dave let out a pained yelp and fell to his knees. A guard dragged him to his feet and shouted, "Hurry up—move it!" while kicking him in the back of the legs until Dave could do nothing but stagger on in a forward motion.

"Soon you will wish you had stayed in your own country with your precious President Kennedy and left us and Fidel Castro alone!" seethed the guard. "You will learn to mind your own business!"

When they at last reached the prison's entrance another group of guards awaited with three more prisoners who appeared more bedraggled than themselves. The six merged, making silent eye contact, bumping into one another, saying nothing but their faces all spoke the same language—fear. Once beyond the building's doorway they were guided down a narrow corridor only lit by a bare bulb now and again. Cobwebs hung like Christmas garlands about the place and the smell of stale air trapped by years behind barred windows mixed with the sour odor of dampness and urine.

At last the party entered a large room which was just as badly lit as the rest of the fetid building. The only pieces of furniture in view were a rickety black desk and an accompanying swivel chair. In it, an obese man sat, squashed in, reading reports Dave assumed contained all the known facts about his group and the other small tangle of men next to them. The guards surrounded the prisoners, grunting for them to move in the fat man's direction.

"My name's Donovan Jones," whispered the big-built whiskery prisoner beside Dave as he was kicked in the butt nastily by a guard.

"Hi," said Dave, thinking it surreal that this guy was trying to engage him in pleasantries at such a time.

The man at the desk tapped a stubby index finger on the file in front of him, whispered something to one of his men and stared at the six men in turn. He was middle-aged with no noticeable neck and a head that seemed to balance precariously atop a beer barrel of a body. His chunky hands twitched faster on the desk in front of him, then he took a deep breath and stood. Barely over 5'5", his sharp facial features and black pin pricks that served for eyes peeked out of folds of flesh and gave an impression of menace, making up for his lack of height. He whispered something else to one of the uniformed men that stood at his side and addressed the captives.

"I am Comandante Emilio Jose Garcia Guerrero, El Comandante of El Castillo del Principe. Americans like you who arrogantly invade our land are held here until we can determine who you are," he looked meaningfully at the six men. "If you represent the FBI or CIA or one of those other organizations that try to assassinate our heroic leader Fidel Castro then you will die. It is as simple as that."

Captain Garcia smiled nastily and his eyes disappeared further into the flesh of his face. He then nodded his head as a signal to his men. With weapons still pointed towards the prisoners, one of the guards went to the door and leaned out into the hallway, where he barked an order into the darkness. Eight or more uniformed men brandishing rifles with bayonets attached to them hurried in from the corridor and stood in front of the captives.

"Strip naked," one of the guards, a tall man with a handlebar moustache, ordered.

The six men were rooted to the spot, not knowing if they had heard the order correctly. Lenny turned to look at Dave, who was staring ahead, his eyes half-closed, no doubt wishing he was anywhere but in this festering hell hole. Donovan Jones and the young blond guy next to him shuffled uncomfortably. Someone tried to whisper something in reply, but Dave was too scared to hear what it was.

"What are you waiting for?" yelled Garcia, making his way through his line of men. "Strip! Now!"

The prisoners hurriedly removed their clothes and stood in the bleak room in their underwear.

"Everything," Garcia growled.

Each prisoner reluctantly pushed their undershorts to their ankles and stepped out of the garments, flipping them to the side with a bare foot. James immediately hid his private parts with his hands, but the others simply stood rooted to the spot, arms hanging at their sides, trembling with dread. Once they were naked, one of the newly arrived Cuban guards lowered his rifle so that his bayonet touched against Dave's scrotum. Another guard lunged his blade forwards until it pricked the flesh of James' penis while his companion jabbed at the limp sack of one of the other captives, who gasped in pain. Dave and Lenny refused to make a sound while James simply stood, tears falling down his face as the guard's blade dug into the side of his penis, drawing a trickle of blood which slid down the shaft.

"Please..." James whispered.

The guard pushed the metal against his skin again, making James scream louder, and said, "Did you speak, pig?"

Following Dave and Lenny, James then bit his lip, realizing that silence was the best policy, but the guards hadn't had their fun yet. They toyed with the six men's privates, digging their bayonets into the skin of their scrotum until blood seeped through their cut flesh. Donovan Jones and his two sidekicks William Taylor with Richard Chase, tried in vain to stay silent, but protests of pain shot out making the guards jeer and laugh. The young blond guy in Jones' group began to cry hysterically as a trickle of urine wound its way through the hairs on his legs and gathered in a pool on the floor.

"Look! The big baby pissed himself!" One of the Cuban men pointed at the puddle, turned his nose up and then pushed the blond prisoner knees down into his own waste.

"Shall I cut this one's cock off?" grinned the tall guard with the big moustache to one of his cronies. His bayonet flicked menacingly across Dave's penis. The other guards shrieked with laughter and egged their colleague on, who was in his element.

"Cut it off!" shouted a short guard with bad skin.

Dave closed his eyes and begged silently for his ordeal to be over. Please not this, anything but this.

"Then feed it to him!" said another guard in broken English, like his cronies.

Dave felt as if he would black out from the terror that paralyzed his body, making him unable to breathe. He could feel the sharpness of the metal nicking his foreskin. He knew that if he reacted or spoke, he would be castrated in seconds.

"Funny, they all seem a little quiet, don't they?" The Comandante smiled at his men. "Nothing to say?" He glared at the captives, as if inviting them to speak.

"Please, I have nothing to do with these men. I was kidnapped at Tamiami Airport, like I said before. Please Comandante Garcia. Sir, I am just a pilot, I'm not CIA." James gabbled on and then

Bill Deane

pointed at Lenny and Dave. "These men forced me here with a gun to my head!" His voice raised into a high-pitched wail.

Garcia laughed and ordered two of his guards to tie a screaming James to a rack against the wall, his arms forcibly stretched outward as the men bound his hands with ropes that were attached to a wooden post which was nailed down with large screws.

"Please, I'm innocent!" James yelled, his eyes almost popping out of his skull as he spotted the whip that Garcia was now running through his fat hands. James begged and cried as the Comandante administered a volley of harsh lashes. The strands of leather ripped across his bare chest and stomach, slicing lines of red through his pale flesh. Lenny's jaw dropped open and the others looked away, too terrified to contemplate the torture that would surely come their way next should they bring attention to themselves too.

But Garcia was a notoriously vicious thug and was enjoying listening to James' screams as each lash landed on his torso. The fat man licked his lips and grunted between each strike. His face sweating and bright red, Garcia gave him another six lashes and stopped, his bulk making him too out of breath to carry on. Pools of sweat had gathered under the arms of his khaki shirt. Garcia caressed the whip enthusiastically, coughed and looked to his men and said, "See, this is what we do with American scum."

James slumped forward, his chin resting on his chest and Dave wasn't sure if he was still alive or not, until he heard a gurgling noise escape from his mouth. Garcia stooped over and rested his hands on his knees, gasping for air. Once he had recovered from his workout, he regained his posture and smiled proudly.

Over and over he strutted up and down the line of six men, demanding to know who they were and if they were CIA spies.

Donovan Jones and his two friends, a small blond guy in his twenties and an older ruddy-faced man who looked like he had had too much sun, denied being CIA. Jones pledged their allegiance to Fidel Castro's cause, admitting that they had traveled to Cuba in order to become defectors. Jones even repeated a famous Che Guevara quote and saluted the Comandante.

"We are your loyal servants," Jones then said, blood seeping from a cut on his lip where he had been punched in the face by one of the guards. "We came here to join you in your brave and just fight."

Garcia's face screwed up into an incredulous ball, his bushy eyebrows almost meeting in a unibrow. "And you expect me to believe this rubbish? This is what a spy would be told to tell us. You think I am stupid?"

Donovan Jones took a tentative step towards the Comandante. He put his hand to his wide chest. "Sir, let me tell you this with the utmost of sincerity.... All my life I've been treated like nothing by America's capitalist system. My two friends and I came here especially to join you and your magnificent leader, Fidel Castro. Isn't that right, William? Alan?" Jones turned to his small gang. The blond young man nodded and threw a pleading look at Garcia through bloodshot eyes. Candles of snot dripped over his lip and blended with the blood that had already caked there.

"Yes sir, it's true, sir, viva Castro!" he said and thumped the air with a tightly-balled fist. Their ruddy-faced friend just looked on timidly, not knowing what to say or do.

Garcia snorted at the three of them and turned to one of his sniggering guards, obviously mimicking the foreign interlopers with exaggerated replica gestures and groveling demeanors.

Garcia was highly suspicious, but was also amused by their fervor. Both he and his comrades spoke in Spanish for a few moments and then all of a sudden Garcia turned to Jones and punched him in the face. His nose made a sickening cracking sound and blood erupted from his nasal canal, spraying down his naked torso. Jones yelled and fell to the floor.

"Shut up!" Garcia shouted. "You are all liars!" He looked at Dave, who was leaning against the wall, next to Jones, who had pulled himself back into a standing position and was using his hand as a bowl, placed under his nose to catch his own blood in.

"And what is your story?" Garcia said.

Dave shuffled uncomfortably under the Comandante's gaze. "Like we told your colleagues back at the army camp, we were just out on a plane ride—a bit of fun, you know? It was a dumb dare," Dave said. "We're not CIA."

Lenny poked his head forward and let out a weak laugh. "I mean, do we look like CIA?"

"When did I tell you to talk?" Garcia's face was now an inch from Lenny's and he jabbed him in the chest with the other end of the whip which he still clutched in his podgy hand. "Did I tell you to speak?"

"No." Lenny gulped and his eyes pointed at the ground.

Garcia's black Army issue boot landed with a great thud in Lenny's bare testicles, sending him screaming and writhing to the floor.

"Get up or you will get another one!" The Comandante ordered. With tears streaming down his face, Lenny dug his fingers into the wall and managed to pull himself onto wobbly legs.

Garcia's face dripped with sweat in the heat of the room and he looked suspiciously at Dave. "A dare? What is this dare?"

"Look we're sorry, Comandante Garcia. Sir," Dave said. "we shouldn't have come here. I dared the others to see if we could get past Cuban radar, and we did. That's it. We were on a day out and bored. We didn't mean any harm."

"You expect me to believe that you are that fucking stupid?" barked Garcia. "No one is that fucking stupid!"

Dave shrugged and nodded sheepishly. "Seems we are. I'm sorry. It was a mistake, that's all." Garcia was about to swipe Dave around the head with the whip but James had caught his attention.

"But...but...sir...I'm not with them! They kidnapped me at gun point. They ordered me to fly to Cuba!" butted in James, now fully awake, but still roped to the wall rack. Garcia sighed heavily and said something to his men in Spanish. Twelve guards surged forward, inches in front of the captives and one of them untied James from the wall, who immediately took a few steps towards the Comandante.

"I've been kidnapped!" he pleaded and fell to his knees, his hands clasped in the praying to God. "Please just let me go! I beg you!"

Garcia simply kicked James in the stomach with his heavy boot, winding his prisoner, who was doubled over, coughing.

"Stop whining like a little girl and stand up!" Garcia then looked at each of the six men, one by one. "I have heard many fairy stories here today. I will find out if you are spies, and if you are, I will enjoy cause you great pain when killing you myself! If any of you are telling the truth, then I won't kill you. It is as simple as that. As the Supreme Commander of El Principe prison and Fidel Castro's loyal soldier, I need time to think about my next moves. Once I have spoken to each of you separately in great detail and to my leader, we will then make our decision based on your performances under questioning. Now get out of my office!"

Once the six had been unceremoniously shoved into a 16-foot-by-12-foot cell, James slunk into the corner, whimpering in pain and holding onto his stomach. Lenny stood next to Dave and the three other prisoners huddled together in the middle of the floor. Huge cockroaches scuttled across the ground, making eerie clicking noises and as Dave's eyes accustomed themselves to the even dimmer light in the cell, he noticed two Cuban-looking men in the far corner of the room. They were both dressed in filthy blood-stained rags and were skin and bones. He wasn't even sure that they were alive until he walked over to them and stooped down, inspecting each one closely. Dave's nose wrinkled under the stench of sweat and human excrement.

"Hi, I'm Dave," he said. The two men stared vacantly ahead, not even registering Dave's presence. One of them rocked back and forth and muttered in Spanish. The other, younger man had blood seeping out of his dead eyes and seemed to be beyond help. Dave noticed that the older man had all his front teeth missing and a flesh wound stretched from his ear to his chin. Dave was well aware that this could be him in a few months if he didn't get out.

Donovan Jones walked up behind a horrified Dave and whispered in his ear, "I'd leave them be, man. They're both fucking crazy. They could be dangerous."

"I gotta get out of this shithole," Dave muttered in a barely audible voice.

"They ain't going to just let us go," replied Jones, still nursing his broken nose. "They got us down as CIA capitalist scum. That

Garcia dude's one evil fat fucker." Jones' tone was grave and he staggered back to his two friends and slumped down on the concrete floor.

Each prisoner had to urinate and defecate in a single hole dug near the centre of the cell, which let off the most obnoxious fumes imaginable and each time Dave squatted to take a dump he had to concentrate on ignoring his strong gagging reflex until he was done.

The men were served slop made out of the skull, brain, guts and excrement of random animals once a day and slept on hard stone as there were no cots in the cell. Twenty-four-seven, guards arrived to drag someone down the corridor for interrogation. The victim would be greeted by Garcia and returned an hour or so later, badly beaten or having undergone electric shock torture.

During the first day at El Principe Dave was the first to receive this special treatment and was pulled from the cell in the middle of the night, taken to a small room at the end of a dark corridor where he had been tied to a wooden bed and had metal probes attached to his scrotum, head and toes.

"Who are you?" Garcia screamed in his face, strings of spit flicking across the air.

"No one. Just a joyrider. It was a dumb mistake..." Dave begged and repeated. Then the buzz of an electric current made a snapping and whirring sound and the smell of burnt flesh and hair permeated the room as Dave's body buckled under the volts surging through his veins. His cries could be heard by those in the cells next door.

Again and again, Garcia repeated the same questions to all six captives, one by one, as they lay shackled to the torture bed, "Who are you?—Who sent you?—Why are you in Cuba?—Are you

CIA?" Each time they were interrogated, Dave and Lenny each stuck to their story, denying being CIA, and they were treated to another beating or dose of electric shock torture. Although James pleaded innocence and maintained that he had been kidnapped by the others, it appeared that Garcia was losing patience. But he was genuinely puzzled as to why these three Americans in cowboy boots looked nothing like usual CIA or FBI agents. He thought they resembled the slouching insolent street kids he had seen on American TV, the ones who listened to rock 'n' roll and hung out on street corners, drinking beer. And as for the other three scruffy interlopers, nothing they said washed with him either. Garcia kept Fidel Castro informed of any events unfolding at El Principe and was aware that Castro too was perplexed over all the differing stories. Garcia was ordered to carry on with the interrogations until one of the men cracked. The Comandante was very pleased to hear this order from his powerful leader. Castro obviously valued his loyalty and trusted his judgment in running such a feared institution. Garcia was proud of El Principe's deadly reputation. He was also greatly enjoying the treatment he had been meting out to his American guests, as he often referred to the six men.

Donovan Jones and his two pals were tortured and beaten in the same manner. And by the third day all six U.S. captives were quivering wrecks, bloody, terrified and almost mad with thirst. Once again, the prisoners resorted to drinking their own urine as the guards refused to answer their pleas for water.

The squalor of the small cell was magnified by the fact that Dave and three of the other men had been suffering terribly with violent sickness and diarrhea from the disgusting concoction they were made to consume, which they soon noticed moved with wriggling maggots and sometimes included a rotting fish that resembled a magnet embedded with pins. But, they had no choice. It was either eat it or die of starvation. Barely managing to hold the bile in as he hurried to the stinking shithole that served as a toilet, Dave joined the other ill men there, where he puked the contents of his guts deep into the black abyss below. No sooner had he finished being sick when he developed a case of the runs and he squatted over the hole with the others, all gripping onto their stomachs as pains seared through their feverish bodies. Only ripped up old newspapers served as toilet paper.

Feeling as if they were teetering on the edge of insanity by the fifth day in El Principe, most of the men just lay on the concrete floor, too exhausted to speak or bother much with one another. Only James could be heard muttering over and over again, "I shouldn't be in here. I want to go home," while he leaned against the wall, his face pressed up against the cold stone.

"Shut up, Eaton. I'm sick of hearing your whining voice," murmured Dave from a corner. Lenny was next to him, slumped forward and holding onto his stomach which churned from the infested gruel he had eaten.

"I don't belong here…" carried on James, banging his head against the wall.

"Be quiet, squealer," mumbled Dave.

"I don't belong here…"

"Shut up!" bellowed Dave, finding some energy from somewhere and lamely pulling himself in James' direction on his backside and kicking his legs out towards the other man, but missing his target who curled into a ball.

"You made me come here." James' plaintive mutterings were

too much for Dave and with any last vestige of strength that he had, he hauled himself onto unstable legs and launched himself at his ex-friend, punching him hard in the face and body. James was too weak to fight and laid there, holding his hands in front of his face as a shield. Dave now squatted on top of James, pulled his fist back and belted James in the mouth once more.

"He isn't worth it, Dave," managed Lenny from his stupor. "Don't waste your energy."

James cried for help as Dave screamed out in wild frustration and pulled his bunched up fist backwards as far as he possibly could. Just as he was about to pummel James in the face again, the door of the dungeon swung open and the tall guard with the moustache stood there casting a shadow across the room. He pointed his Kalashnikov at the men, who were all frozen to the spot, eyes wide with confusion.

"Get up, all of you," the guard commanded and motioned at Dave's group and the other trio of prisoners. The two Cuban men in the corner were too far gone to notice what was happening and remained where they were, dazed and mumbling.

"Prepare to leave El Principe," the guard announced.

Dave untangled himself from a half-comatose James and managed to pull himself into a standing position. His once boyish face was a mass of cuts and bruises from all the beatings he had. He squinted under the dim light from the prison doorway.

"Where are we going?" he managed to ask and glanced at Lenny with fear. Dave knew he could take no more torture. He'd rather the guard just put a bullet through his head there and then.

The guard smiled, then pointed his weapon at Riley. "Just you wait and see American pig. Now get moving!"

ELEVEN

I T WAS FRIDAY AFTERNOON, April 20, 1962. Joey Green, pretty much a novice in the news business of WGBS, had just finished his 4:30PM newscast when minutes later checked the multiple bells signaling a bulletin on the UPI wire. Another hijack to Cuba. He thought, so many of them. But wait, Castro's sending the skyjackers, two of them, back to Miami. Castro never did that before. This is interesting. James Eaton, the pilot, says he was ordered at gunpoint to fly the two to Cuba. The skyjackers were David Riley and Leonard Owen released along with pilot Reggie Doan.

"I know all these guys," Joey said aloud to himself, "not Doan, but the rest of them. They kept coming to WFUN trying to get airplay for Riley. But wait, who's this guy Reggie Doan and what happened to Eaton?"

Now the AP bulletin: "Riley and Owen wanted to defect to Cuba and under the new Air Piracy Act, the pair could get death in the electric chair."

"This is crazy," Green thought. "These guys spent their time with booze and looking for broads on Miami Beach. That's it. They never talk about Cuba or politics. "

Green runs into the main newsroom and blurts out, "This is an important story!"

News Director Spencer Ganes takes the bulletins out of Green's hands. "You know how many Cuban skyjackings there have been, Green? It happens about once a week, particularly on a Friday when some lonely guy from New York or Chicago, wants to captivate a bunch of passengers." The newsmen writing their upcoming casts concentrate on their typewriters as Ganes explains what is and what isn't news. "There's no interest in this Green because it happens all the time. It doesn't relate to anybody in our Miami audience."

"But I know these guys."

"Do you think the audience is interested that you know them? In fact, I wouldn't want to admit that I personally knew a couple of defectors who left this country to become communists!"

"But they flew there in a small plane, not a DC-7."

"Well, you've found something different, but who the hell cares? It's Friday afternoon and everybody's thinking of the weekend and not the communist troublemaker in Cuba. It's a non-story. Don't write it. You hear me?"

Green followed Dane's directive, but was puzzled over the inconsistency. They weren't communists. He just knew it. But then why were they caught in Cuba? Dave Riley, who told everybody he managed everything in his life, was now facing charges of an international skyjacking and could wind up in the electric chair. Green, still puzzled decided it was better to stay out of this mystery.

Castro had let them go. He never released anyone back to the

States for prosecution if he even had an inkling that they were spying in his country. He usually killed or indefinitely imprisoned those thought to be guilty of such practices. Under the tough, newly revised Air Piracy Act, Dave and Lenny could get the death penalty in the electric chair in Stark, Florida. However hard Green tried to work out what was going on, he couldn't and his more seasoned and jaded work colleagues showed little interest in Joey's excitement.

THE SKYJACKING INFECTION WAS underway until the desire to defect escalated between 1968 and 1972 with 117 gunpoint and bomb threat attempts occurring on American airlines with 3/4ths of them taking the typical trip to Havana. President Nixon's order to install metal detectors at airports and Castro's eventual agreement to punish skyjackers cut the forced flights to Cuba to near extinction.

But before all this was put in place, in May 1961, an incident which inaugurated the opening of the modern skyjacking era happened, when Antulio Ortiz, a Miami electrician decided he was bored with his wife. Ortiz wanted to find a new one, where in his opinion the most beautiful women in the world lived—Cuba. Instead of traveling there by booking a normal seat on a plane via Montreal or Mexico City like anyone else would have, he took a revolver on board a passenger flight and seized the jet, ordering the pilot to fly to Cuba, where it landed safely in Havana. It wasn't reported whether he found the woman of his dreams, but it is thought that he must have, as he never returned to Miami and his discarded wife. No one heard from Ortiz again.

DURING THE MORNING OF the next day, Dave Riley and
Leonard Owen flew into Miami International Airport on a specially
approved Pan American flight with a direct route from Havana to
Miami. Dave and the other four captives were immediately arrested
by FBI agents and then shoved, visibly bruised from the week of
torture, in front of a gang of reporters waiting for them at a press
conference in the main building at Miami International, just a mile
or so from where it all started one week before at the Tamiami
business airport.

The CIA, the only major agency in the Federal Government
without a public relations department, refused to talk to the press
in any capacity. However, the media savvy FBI, presented itself as
pleased to run the busy news conference along with Dave and the
other men they had arrested fresh off the flight. Wesley G. Grapp,
FBI agent in charge, had been waiting for them when the plane
landed.

"Welcome home, guys," he smiled, swinging several sets of
handcuffs.

Knowing about the fuss awaiting their operatives, Dave and
Lenny had been carefully briefed and starkly warned by the CIA
sometime between leaving El Principe and landing on U.S. soil to
keep their mouths shut and just do as they're told or else.

The place was buzzing with paparazzi and eager journalists,
wanting any scoop on the perpetrators. Grapp and his agents
silently ushered Dave and Lenny, alongside Donovan Jones and
his two shipmates, Richard and William into the large room at
the back of the airport which was packed with journalists, sitting
on lines of metal fold-up chairs, clasping paper cups of vending
machine coffee.

Just a few yards behind Dave and Lenny followed a young dark haired man in a smart shirt and tie. Lenny and Dave threw a quick glance at one another which said, "who the hell is this?" The dark haired guy was then told to stand next to a middle-aged FBI agent behind a makeshift podium to address the press. He was introduced by Grapp as the pilot of the Cessna on the fateful skyjacking day, newly dubbed *Black Friday,* as it all started on Friday the 13th. His name was Reginald Doan. There was no sign of James Eaton at the press conference and he wasn't so much as mentioned. The FBI ostensibly had no idea of his existence.

Grapp then confirmed to the media, "David Thomas Riley, a freelance song writer from Coral Gables, and Leonard Malcolm Owen, a doughnut salesman, from Orlando, were under arrest for kidnapping Reginald Doan and his single engine Cessna on Friday, April the 13th, 1962, when the men ordered him to fly to Havana during what was meant to be a sightseeing and movie-making trip around south Florida." He went on to confirm that the three had subsequently been held for questioning together by the Cubans for a week. Grapp took a couple of steps to the side and nodded at Doan, who took his place at the small podium.

Dave and Lenny remembered their stern orders to be quiet and remained silent. Looking down at the black metal desk at which they were seated, Dave fiddled with a stray ballpoint that had rolled in front of him. Doan, however, was very talkative for some reason unknown to Dave. And then, it dawned on him, like a huge gaping epiphany what was going on. He would have laughed aloud if he could have, but there were photographers pointing cameras at him. This young Reginald Doan character was a CIA plant. It was now his and Lenny's job to keep their heads down and let Doan explain, or they could end up like James Eaton. He had to hand it to the Feds, they weren't dumb or backwards in coming forward.

DAVE TOLD GREEN AT their Cuban restaurant meeting, all he knew was that after Garcia and the Cubans had let them out of El Principe and had bundled them onto the Pan Am flight to Miami, James had somehow disappeared along the way to the airport. He didn't know exactly when or how and never found out what did happen. It was as if James had vaporized into a mist. Dave recalled a lot of activity between the prison and the airport. They had been forced into various rooms and vehicles. There was lots of activity and shouting in Spanish, only he could never pinpoint when he lost sight of Eaton, nor could Lenny. It wasn't until they were on the way to Havana Airport that they were told they weren't about to be shot, but rather Castro had ordered their release. Dave, so relieved felt like sobbing his thanks, wanted to ask why, however his sensible side told him to keep it shut and just get out of there.

It was pretty obvious to Dave that James' loose lips and phony story had scared the hell out of the CIA. There was no way they needed someone lying and spouting off about being kidnapped by two guys, especially a guy hired out of Dade County Jail to carry out their missions. If the world at large and the American public had found out that the CIA spent months training felons from a cushy pad in the local penitentiary to spy for the government, their necks would be on the line, ands o would President Kennedy's. The practice of freed criminals on the loose, put the public in immense personal danger and this mess leaking out was not an option for the Feds. James Eaton had done a disappearing act like so many before and following in the early 60s.

As for Dave, he had his answer, straight after his arrest at Miami International. Castro had believed his and Lenny's fairy story, that they were joy-riders on a dare, just as Dave and Lenny kept saying throughout electric shock torture. Though there was also the possibility that Castro knew they were CIA plants and instead of shooting them, wanted to watch a CIA dance. To create a cover, the Feds declared a kidnapping.

In the end, Castro had ordered El Principe's Garcia to release them and send them back to the U.S.A. along with Donovan Jones and his two friends, who's story was they had stolen their boss's $40,000 shrimper boat named the *Teresa and Julian* from near Key West to sail to Cuba to join the clandestine Castro overthrow. It was assumed at the time that Fidel Castro was sick of them and glad to be rid of the whole stupid bunch of degenerates.

To the FBI and press, six men returned on that Pam Am flight on Saturday April 21, yet one had somehow undergone a dramatic change in identity before arriving at the airport. Reginald Doan even had the scared victim act down to a fine art. He had been well briefed by the Feds, and very quickly for that matter. Dave and Lenny watched this guy with the crisp blazer and expensive shoes, who was now claiming to have been kidnapped by them and interrogated alongside them in El Principe Prison. Dave considered during the press conference and later on their way to Dade County Jail for further questioning that this CIA plant resembled a squeaky clean momma's boy, but it was all a ruse. As he addressed the news conference, running his hands through his neat brown hair, he was smooth, confident in his story, cleared his throat all with a slight tremor in his voice. He was obviously well rehearsed.

The *Miami Herald* writer, Gene Miles, had his pen poised at the ready and got it all down for his article—verbatim. Reginald Doan began, "It was supposed to be just a local demonstration flight, and then this guy stuck a 38 caliber pistol in my neck under my right ear." Doan did the actions with an invisible weapon at this point. "I thought it was a joke at first. We were just off Miami Beach." Doan's bottom lip trembled a little as he scanned the huddle of journalists in the room. Dave expected tears to spring from his earnest eyelids, but they never did. Doan carried on, "He told me to fly to Cuba and I saw the bullets in the chamber and I was so scared that I almost jumped out."

A journalist shot his hand in the air, eager to ask a question, but Doan continued, rattled by his memories of a particularly unlucky Friday the 13th, "I said something silly like 'you know it's against federal regulations to hijack a plane,' but then shut up. They knew what they were doing. They'd planned it. The big guy, the one who called himself James Eaton, was pretty intelligent." Doan motioned his head towards Lenny. "The other one identified himself as David Riley of Coral Gables."

So, the rest of the phony CIA story was that Leonard Owen was using an alias during this skyjacking, to cover the fact that the real pilot, James Eaton, was actually missing and should have returned to the U.S. with the others. So nobody would notice that James Eaton had gone AWOL. No questions asked. No need to go searching for Eaton or talk to the Cubans about where he was.

Dave had to give it to the Feds, they were damn smart. They had briefed this Doan guy down to the last minute detail. In a weird way, he felt kind of proud to be employed by such an outfit, even if he did realize that his current situation wasn't exactly ideal for him. He was looking at life in prison or a seat on the electric chair, but Dave had a warped sense of priority. His ego made sure of it.

The CIA story sold to the press and public at large over the following months was that Dave Riley and Leonard Owen were defectors, allegedly supporters of Communism. Reginald Doan kept his side of the story with the CIA. Dave put a silent bet on it that it wasn't the first time Doan had lied for the Agency. He was too confident. Dave also bet that the kid wasn't short of a few bucks either. He was pretty young to be a pilot employed by the Feds. Something about Reginald Doan secretly impressed him. Maybe he was a little envious.

Riley deduced that the Feds had placed Doan somewhere in the Miami airport just as their Pan Am flight landed and mixed him in with the unfolding furor, so he'd be picked up by the FBI too. Dave didn't know how they had done it, but it was sneaky and clever, he had to admit. The CIA must have also released the second news wire to the press themselves the late afternoon before, which removed James' name as the pilot of the plane and replaced it with Reginald Doan's. He would now be heading into the courtroom to take his place on the witness stand to tell the world the truth.

There was never any mention of James Eaton again, by the CIA, FBI or in the press reports. Whatever happened to him, no one knew. He simply vanished from the face of the earth.

Dave, Lenny and Reginald were ushered out of the airport conference room and into another part of the building until the FBI took them to Miami Dade County Jail for further questioning, where Dave and Lenny were charged and Reginald Doan was released. Joey Green closely followed daily coverage of the case on broadcast news and in the papers. Doan even wrote a piece about what he titled "His Terrifying Experience" for the *Herald* himself, but it had been tidied up by staff writer. A pen pusher tucked away in a quiet corner of a CIA office somewhere had probably written the article for Doan.

Dave later told Green that if anyone deserved to win an Oscar for his performance during that whole period it was Reginald Doan. "Humphrey Bogart couldn't have done any better." said Dave, and Dave idolized Bogie.

When the case hit the newspapers, TV and radio, the individual journalists who had been at the news conference, the police and the American public had no idea they had been duped by the CIA and their 23-year-old stool pigeon.

TWELVE

—————

ONE AFTERNOON IN THE ancient world, a frog sat by
a river, basking in the sun. He had nearly drifted into a
deep sleep when he heard something stirring in the nearby woods.
Nervous, the frog glanced up and saw one of the most feared of
all creatures, a scorpion, making its way toward him. Knowing of
the poison the scorpion carried inside and that a single sting meant
certain death, the frog froze in fear as the scorpion angled itself in
front of the frog and halted.

"Why do you look so scared?" the scorpion asked.

Barely able to form words, the frog wept "Because on this
beautiful day, rich with life, I don't want to die."

"Don't be ridiculous," the scorpion chided. "Why would I want
to kill you?"

The frog admitted that he had no good answer. "I can't eat you.
I don't hate you. You mean me no harm. Why then would I consider
killing you?"

"Good point," the frog answered, relaxing a little.

"In fact, I want to ask you a favor. I'd like to be on the other side of the river but I can't swim. If I were to hop on your back, would you carry me across?" The frog shivered at the thought.

"But if I were to do that, I would be completely vulnerable to your sting."

"Are you crazy?" the scorpion roared. "If I were to do that while we were crossing, I would immediately drown."

The frog thought the whole thing through, realizing that the scorpion must mean what he said. Besides, it would be in the frog's best interest to have the scorpion for a friend. "Alright, then," the frog cheerfully said.

The scorpion smiled, hopped up on the frog's back, and they began to cross the river...

THOUGH JOEY NEVER AGAIN visited the Cuban café, on February 9, 1964, he did get together with Dave one final time. They met at a decrepit movie theatre in downtown Miami. Dave called to say that a double-feature had been scheduled for a one-time showing of movies about to be removed indefinitely from distribution so this was their last chance to catch them. They'd never met before for a film, yet Joey didn't give the matter much thought until they were seated in middle of a clammy bijou.

"See that guy over there?" Dave whispered.

"Yeah," Joey replied just as the auditorium darkened while the brittle chain of celluloid began to whir through an ancient projector back in the booth.

"Raymond Hooper—I know for a fact that the first flick up happens to be his all-time favorite movie."

Momentarily, Joey drew a blank. Raymond who? As the first

grey images appeared onscreen, Joey recalled where he'd heard that name. Sitting three rows ahead and to their left was the man David Riley had tried to shake down at the Coral Gables bus station back in June, 1960.

Suddenly, the 1953 film's title read. Joey watched as big, solid Sterling Hayden portrayed the top cop in a small California town. All at once the scene cut away to a middle class home on a nearby hill where a family went about their daily business until the front bell rang. The mom opened the door to three men in dark suits, a cruel-eyed Frank Sinatra their leader. He explained that they were G-men assigned to check out the area; the President of the U.S. would shortly pass by down below, unannounced, on a train. Quickly, it became clear these men were hired killers; Sinatra unpacked a long range rifle he'd use to assassinate the President from this secluded spot up on a grassy knoll.

"So Joey, it's time to complete your education." They were seated in a booth at a diner near the theatre between movies, ready for coffee and conversation following the first show.

"Yes, teacher—go on."

"That Friday the 13th flight to Cuba I had a little role in. The code-name was *Black Friday*."

"After you guys got caught and things turned dark—"

"No, from day one. Any idea what 'black' means to the intelligence community?"

Joey shook his head no.

"Secret! There's no more important word to those guys."

"You're referring to the CIA?"

"Tip of the iceberg," Dave scoffed. "Before I say more, you sure wanna take on the responsibility of knowing?"

"Knowing what?"

"The name of the group that really runs this country."

Green scared shitless by this, but like the moth drawn to the flame, couldn't resist. If someone offered him a million bucks to get up and walk out of there at that moment, he couldn't do it. "Go ahead. Tell me."

Riley leaned across the table, stretching almost to Joey's left ear before hissing: "The 54/12 Group." The phrase sounded innocuous enough.

"That's it?"

Riley pulled back to his place on the padded bench, eyes dancing wickedly. "Kid, that's everything! 54/12 first came into being halfway through *Bay of Pigs* when Bissell and several other top honchos from politics and the military begged—and I mean begged—Kennedy to let them go back in again. See, bad as things were, we still coulda won."

But this is Dee Thomas—David Riley—David Montez—not one man but three—each crazier than the next—Joey must remember that—still that doesn't necessarily mean he isn't right about this.

"So you're telling me that the CIA whacked Kennedy because the President made a dumb call with *Bay of Pigs*?"

"I'm saying nothing of the sort. The Agency isn't so fucked in the head that it doesn't understand people are fallible. Everyone deserves a second chance. Right?"

"Right."

"First, Kennedy placed all the blame on the CIA. The whole thing was their baby, their fault. He, pure as a new-born lamb. Then came *The Cuban Missile Crisis*. Do I need to tell you about that?"

"No need at all." That was the incident in which Joey had redeemed himself from his failure to speak out first on *Bay of Pigs* by providing an in-depth daily commentary on what went down between October 8 and 14, 1962—top flight work that brought Green to the attention of the networks.

"See, Castro assumes the *Bay of Pigs* had merely been wave one—next time, the entire American military would come at him. Up until then, Fidel had been nervous about Russia as an ally, fearing they were no better than the U.S., so if he let Kruschev move men and machinery onto his Cuban soil, before he'd know it the Soviets would be running the place. Castro had turned down one offer after another from the Premier. Now, though, it came down to a matter of his survival. After the *Bay of Pigs*, Castro finally came to hate the Americans as completely as the Russians had since 1945. Nuclear missiles in Cuba, pointed at the U.S.? Great idea! That'll stop JFK from even thinking of attacking again. With a deterrence like that, Cuba can peacefully go about its own business.

But, Castro seriously underestimated Kennedy—or more correctly, failed to grasp how delicate JFK's position was following the recent debacle. If the President hoped to regain his image as an intellectual warrior and win re-election, he had to talk tough, stand firm, be strong. For once, he did just that. Dismissing the CIA, who, in his mind, was responsible for the failure of the *Bay of Pigs*. Kennedy decided this time around he'd do it himself. If the missiles were not removed immediately, he would, under the old *Monroe Doctrine*, assume the Russians had declared war. Someone had to give and Kruschev blinked. The missiles were removed and JFK reinstated as our young hero-president—no sooner was the crisis over than Jack and Bobby, basking in their success, asked each other: 'What the fuck do we need the CIA for? Maybe it's time to phase it out.' Besides, now that we've shown Castro who's boss, perhaps it's time to normalize relations. Obviously, he's there to stay. Why cut off our nose to spite our face? Let's learn to live with the guy, open up lines of communication."

"The CIA couldn't have liked that much."

"You're putting it too mildly. Now, imagine how the anti-Castro Cubans here in Florida felt? Until then, Kennedy had been their savior. Overnight he transformed into Satan."

"Plus, they still had connections with the CIA."

"You're almost there, kid."

"At that moment, Kennedy's fate was sealed."

Dropping his eyes, Dave shook his head. "Not quite."

"What more can there be?"

"Absolutely certain you wanna know, Joey?"

"Not particularly—but, I have to."

Dave's eyes twinkled. "Sure. Like that poet/philosopher you once quoted to me? How did that go again..."

"The end of man is to know."

"Right! So, college boy, who else believed Kennedy had betrayed them?"

The answer hit Joey like a lightning bolt. "The Mob."

"Bobby Kennedy, America's District Attorney went after 'the boys' with everything he had."

"But it was Jack, not Bobby, who went down hard."

"Sure, see, there's a Sicilian saying: 'Never stop a snake by cutting off its tail. Go for the head.' Bobby was the tail, thrashing around. Word to shut down the Mob came to him from Big Brother.

With Jack gone, Bobby became a non-entity. Let him live out his pathetic little life. Unless he ever makes the mistake of running for President."

"And that, as they say, is that." Joey sighed, wondering could all this be true or was this the biggest line of bullshit Riley ever handed out.

"Not quite."

"There's one more piece to the jigsaw puzzle?"

Dave nodded, "To those in the know, it's called The Sinatra Connection. Following his big comeback in the mid-1950s, in the wake of an Oscar nod for *From Here to Eternity*, and the release of a series of melancholic albums from Capitol that revealed the former bubbly pop-star as the world's greatest saloon singer, Sinatra overnight transformed into our premier superstar. After Bogart died, the so-called Rat Pack—Hollywood's heavyweights— came to surround Sinatra as their new 'Chairman of the Board.' This led to well-publicized late night brawls in Las Vegas bars in which they acted like street thugs with money and power. Yet there was something schizophrenic about all of it. For by daylight, Sinatra fiercely dedicated himself to the burgeoning Civil Rights movement. When Sinatra played the Sands, Sammy Davis Jr. was right there with him. No one had a problem with that, but Sinatra took it further. If he stayed at that hotel casino, he didn't want Sammy segregated over in some run down motel on the edge of town, as it always had been. Sinatra threatened to pull the plug on the Rat Pack shows unless Sammy got his own suite too. The top brass had a hard time with that, but if you wanted Frank, you took the package. The Sands boys swallowed hard when they agreed, the color barrier was broken in Vegas. A swinger bachelor at 40 plus,

Sinatra lived out the myth, even then being popularized by Hugh Hefner—The Playboy Philosophy, all ready to go mainstream during the early 1960s.

Meanwhile, Sinatra had always enjoyed playing ball with 'the big guys,' those who presided over the dark and light sides of the American Dream. The former, he'd aligned himself with in his youth. Top mafioso, Sam Giancana, was the man who assured that young Frank sang in all Mob-owned music venues. And, after Sinatra's star began to wane, Sam used his muscle to land his boy Frankie the role that won him an Academy Award when the studio bosses had wanted anyone but him. Maybe a horse's head did turn up in some producer's bed—or maybe that just might be a myth. One way or the other, Giancana's message came across. Billed right up there alongside Burt Lancaster and Monty Clift was Frank Sinatra.

Frankie, though, had bigger ambitions. He wanted to have it both ways. The moment he met Jack Kennedy, it was love at first sight. The young politician and the suave singer were already emerging as key icons for the upcoming decade. Why shouldn't they pal around? The kid from the wrong side of Hoboken wanted respectability, and hanging around with a bright Ivy League liberal, likewise dedicated to Civil Rights, played into his plan. Kennedy got plenty out of the deal, too, including the world's most popular entertainer as his unofficial campaign manager. Sinatra had *High Hopes* rewritten as the Kennedy theme song during the 1960 face-off with sitting vice-president Dick Nixon. While Jack introduced Frankie to the fashionable set, Sinatra helped Kennedy slip off for his secret walks on the wild side and then an introduction to Marilyn Monroe led to a hot and heavy affair.

There were those in the Rat Pack, Dean Martin in particular, who didn't approve of this. To Dino's way of thinking, Kennedy had seduced Sinatra into becoming the Bostonian's L.A. pimp. But when Dino attempted, treading with understandable caution, to broach the subject, Frank waved him away. 'This guy's as good a pal as you are. I trust him like a brother. And just think! Once he's in the White House, we'll hang out there. Ain't that a kick in the head?'

Then word reached Sinatra, indirectly through Kennedy's aged father Joseph, that the potential President needed a favor. Frankie's barnstorming was certainly appreciated, but that might not be enough to put Jack over the top. Some States they were going to win, others they'd lose. The final decision would come down to two and, even more specifically, two districts of Chicago. Was it possible Mr. Sinatra might speak to Mr. Giancana? The syndicate had always operated out of Chicago, which it controlled. Might something be done? Frankie, still a naive kid at heart, despite that cruel, cynical, hardened facade, all but danced with delight. To be the go-between, the link between the next President and the Mob—the rush! Sinatra as the kingpin—the king maker—the ultimate power broker."

"But, how did Giancana come to trust father Jo? It's a bit of a stretch."

"Sinatra gave his word. Staked his life on it. 'This guy's become like a brother to me,' he told Giancana."

"Dave, JFK was no fool! Certainly, he'd know there'd be responsibilites associated with doing business with the Mob?"

"You would think, but no sooner had the Kennedy era begun than Frankie was being wined and dined in the White House.

Jack's wife didn't care much for him, so Sinatra came to think of Jacqueline as a snob, turned off by him being Italian, and in showbiz to boot. Actually, Jacqueline Bouvier Kennedy cared not a whit about anyone's ethnicity or profession, so long as it was legal. From day one, Jackie pegged Sinatra as a pimp at heart, orchestrating her husband's wild carousing with high scale whores, telling themselves they were 'serious actresses.'

Jacqueline Bouvier had been born with class. JFK married her to align her blueblood status with his own nouveau-riche arrogance and high-flying ambition. 'I am going to be the first Irish-Catholic President of the United States.' Sinatra knew so little about what class really meant, yet so hungered to achieve it that he fully believed a Kennedy connection could make his own American Dream come true.

As for Giancana, once the election was a done deal he planned to make use of Frankie's position in Kennedy's unofficial cabinet. A student of Machiavelli, Giancana devised a scheme that would put him in a position he'd always hoped for—the puppet master behind the scenes who called all the shots that went down in America. First they hooked Jack up with Marilyn. She hungered for class and thought that banging the President would allow her that. He wanted to fuck a fantasy right out of a movie. Neither was fully satisfied, but then who ever is when a dream becomes reality? Marilyn got Jack talking and passed all that he said on to Frankie, who in turn delivered it to Sam. Then Marilyn made the mistake of falling in love with Jack and complained that she felt guilty. At about the same time, Jack passed her on to Bobby, who was elated for a while until he too realizes what a slob she was and wanted out. Since she knew enough to be dangerous to the Mob as well as those in the Oval Office, 'the boys' took care of her, along with their contacts at the CIA, and in doing so supposedly cemented their friendship with the White House.

That didn't prove to be true, though. Sam still wanted someone on the inside. So a girl named Judith Campbell, briefly hitched to a B-movie actor named Billy Campbell, had been lured into the Mob's circle of friends. Old as he was, Giancana had enjoyed her on more than one occasion. The bizarre thing was, Judith looked like Jacqueline Kennedy's evil twin. If Jackie had been born poor and desperate, she'd have been Judith Campbell. A genius at human personality, Sam understood a guy like Jack could never resist fucking his cold, aloof wife's double. That'd turn him on even more than Marilyn, Jayne Mansfield, and the other blondes Sinatra had already set Jack up with. In the unique mind of JFK, this would constitute the perfect revenge against Jackie, part and parcel of America's gentry, for having stooped so low as to marry the descendant of an Irish thief. How had Groucho Marx put it? 'I'd never want to belong to a club that would stoop so low as to admit someone like me into it.' Maybe that's what drew Kennedy to Sinatra? If there had been a contest to determine the most self-loathing man in America, the epic bout between them would have ended in a tie.

Once more, then, Sam and Frankie huddled. Introduce your President pal to this babe. Soon as they hit the sack, Judy will have JFK wrapped around her little finger. When the fucking's finished, they'll talk. Oh, how they'll talk! Judy will know what to ask. Kennedy will think she's his new best friend and secret lover—his confidante—and the Mob will have a direct line to the White House—thanks to Frank! For a while, it worked out as old Sam planned. Whatever might be coming up next for the Administration, he knew about before the Secretary of State or the head of the CIA. More than once, Giancana passed on info Judy fed on to him and then to Dulles, and by then the CIA was recruiting guys like me out of jail cells in Dade County to run cowboy missions from Florida to Cuba.

Then something went terribly wrong. One day Judy, bratty bitch that she could be, said the wrong thing to Jack. Made some little slip that caused Kennedy to realize he was being had. That was it! Jack kicked her out of his bed and his life. Since Kennedy now knew Judy had been a Mob set-up and that the culprit behind the plant was Sinatra, 'The Chairman of the Board' became a non-entity—someone from which Jack had to disengage. Gradually, the doors of the White House were closed to Frank Sinatra. Something of a naive kid at heart, Frankie didn't initially get it. Figured maybe his pal Jack was too busy with international stuff to hang out. Then Frankie heard JFK would be coming to Palm Springs in March '62 for a getaway, leaving Jackie back in D.C., of course, which meant a week of wild whoring. This would be just like old times! Without checking first, Sinatra spent big money, hundreds of thousands, remodeling his West Coast compound so there'd be enough room for the President's entire entourage. Then he learned through the grapevine that Kennedy would be staying at Bing Crosby's home. Insult of insults, as Bing represented Frankie's only competition for the title of "Greatest Singer Living," and worse still, Bing was a Republican! This invisible slap in the face would in time, pass. The problem was, it didn't end there.

JFK could have gotten away with dumping both Sinatra and Giancana cold. That wasn't his way—not in Kennedy's nature—

Jack wanted blood and he set out to get it. He and brother Bobby, now Attorney General, huddled in the Oval Office and came up with precisely the right punishment for this invasion of Jack's privacy. Two days later, Robert F. Kennedy, Jr., up until then loudly insisting he would shut down the Ku Klux Klan, announced that the Justice Department was about to mount a massive war on organized crime. The Mob would be rooted out, destroyed, a terrible blight banished from our national landscape. This was now his mission for the good of American people. Actually, a selfish act of vengeance for the Kennedys.

Now, old Sam, reading a newspaper while seated in his own oval office, decides the Kennedy boys have gone too far: 'You want blood? Fine! Understand, though blood will have blood."

"...And no one betrays the family."

"You got it, kid! Now Frankie wept like a child to Old Sam begging for forgiveness and accepting of the consequences of his misjudgement of the Kennedy boys."

"So, Frankie was in deep water with the bosses."

"Right, only Frankie was like a son to Sam—and how could a father not forgive his beloved boy for being gullible?"

"But, someone had to pay. If not Frankie, then..."

"Exactly. You see, Joey, that was the only time the Mob ever hit a cop or politician. If such men were honest and went out to bring you down, 'the boys' just had to live with that. Elliot Ness in Chicago, the thirties? Forget what you see on TV. Not one shot was ever fired at The Untouchables. Thomas Dewey, New York, the forties? Everyone was scared shitless he might shut 'em down, but when Louis Lepke, one of their own, got so frustrated he confided to some friends he was thinkin'—just thinkin' mind you—of hittin'

Dewey and word reached the top, you know what came down? Luciano and Lansky said Lepke had to go. Killed by his buddies for threatening to blow away a man out to get them all. You had to live with the pain such men caused. These are rules of the game. On the other hand, if they dealt with you, fine, but if they dared pull an outright betrayal—then came the 'Final Solution.'"

"One final question, Dave. Kennedy wasn't dumb by a long shot. He must have known that you don't mess with the Mob, so why would he do something so obviously self-destructive?"

"A-ha!" Riley's eyes lit up, "Finally, you have asked me the one question I can't answer."

"You don't know?"

"Whatever the reason, JFK took it with him to the grave."

"Alright then, so now I know what happened. How many other people know about this? "

"You. Me. A dozen other people, tops."

"So, what do you want me to do with all this information?"

"Well, kid, you are a journalist."

"A responsible one. I can't proceed without proof."

"So, then, when will the public know? A hundred years from now—Maybe it won't take that long. "

"When all those who participated in *Bay of Pigs* are dead, gone, and can't be prosecuted. Perhaps fifty."

"Bits and pieces will slip out sooner, but you're right—fifty years!"

"By who?"

David T. Riley cast Joey Green that ear-to-ear shit eatin' grin for the final time ever, "I dunno. Maybe you..."

Joey paused to consider before replying. "Maybe."

THE MANCHURIAN CANDIDATE, THE second movie, also starred Frank Sinatra. It had been released in the fall of '62. Joey had heard that it was terrific, very offbeat because it dealt with the subject of mind control, but was otherwise distracted as he silently sorted through Dave's words. If true, how could have Riley been privileged to such top secret information? Green, recognizing truth, more often than not, is stranger than fiction, considered perhaps this one man of at least three aliases was not a fantasist after all. He walked away from his last meeting with Dave confounded yet resolved in knowing that if there was any validity to the stories of Dee Thomas—David Riley—David Montez, the pieces would eventually come together in due time.

Joey later realized that *The Manchurian Candidate* was a companion piece, if unintentionally, to *Suddenly*. This time around, Sinatra played the good guy, a Korean war vet who discovers one of his men, brainwashed by the Commies while held prisoner, is determined to kill a candidate for the presidency. Sinatra sets out to stop the man and they confront one another at the convention as the nominating process takes place. In the film, we never learn the precise reason why this man has to go, what he has done, or to whom. In the end, that doesn't matter. What does count is that two films, each of which predicted an era of assassinations to be right around the corner, were pulled from distribution shortly after the assassination of the President. As Joey would later learn, this apparently happened at the direct request of Frank Sinatra.

SO THE FROG SWAM across the river with the scorpion on its back. When they reached the halfway point, the frog felt a sudden stirring on his back, followed by a terrible pain as the scorpion plunged his stinger deep into the frog's soft flesh. The pain soon passed. In its place arrived a gradual hardening of the body as well as a darkening of his vision. This, the frog realized, is my moment of death!

"But I am not your enemy," the frog cried out.

"I know," the scorpion sadly replied.

"And when momentarily I die, you will drown."

"That's right," the scorpion wailed.

"There is no logic to it."

"None whatsoever."

"Why, then, did you just kill me? Quick! Before I die, I want—I need—to know."

The scorpion attempted to explain in that brief moment they both had left. "Because," the scorpion said, himself truly understanding for the first time, "it was my nature."

THIRTEEN

U S DISTRICT JUDGE EMMET Clay Cooke made his way across the courtroom and took center place on the bench. Dave and Lenny stood next to one another, in front of Cooke, side by side in white shirts and slim-line ties. The judge had a commanding presence and a tone in his voice that reminded all attending that he was in charge. He faced the young fresh-faced lawyer representing the accused.

"How do the defendants plead?" Cooke asked, leaning his elbows on the wooden ledge of the bench in front of him, his black cloak barely hiding the worn tweed jacket and crew neck sweater underneath. His graying hair, like the man himself, had a mind of its own, reaching out at the sides over his ears, and black-framed eye glasses perched on the bridge of his long nose.

Cooke had been a judge for over 30 years. The court room was his domain, his living room almost, and he had long since left behind the need or inclination to worry unduly about his appearance or image. In his view, he was his own person.

"Not guilty," Alvin Goldberg, representing the accused,

responded to all charges.

Cooke didn't look up from the papers in front of him, instead grunting twice in reply to the much younger man's words, all the while poring over documents from his elevated position on the bench. He shuffled the papers dramatically and carried on, mumbling quietly and chewing the inside of his cheek as he read. Everyone in the courtroom silently waited for his pronouncement, journalists and spectators in the public gallery, as well as court clerks, lawyers and the accused themselves.

Dave gulped, hoping that this would be it and he'd be out of there, going about his own business as usual, but the judge had a reputation of which even Dave was aware. Cooke's long record of decision-making added up to a bizarre ensemble of unpredictable judgments over his impressive career. It was impossible to fathom how the man's mind worked.

"Hmmm," Cooke mumbled to himself, while sizing up the two accused men with his grey-blue eyes, both trying to appear as innocent as possible. Dave let a sweet smile slip across his lips, which was swiftly wiped away when he saw Cooke openly glaring at him. He was studying Dave hard, but Dave found his face unreadable. Riley tried his best not to fidget. Lenny looked down at the floor with an expression of someone about to meet his maker. A couple of journalists in the gallery mumbled to one another. Cooke looked over at them until they stopped and sheepishly grew silent. The judge scratched at his head and swept his unruly hair back with both hands, playing for time. And then, suddenly, Cooke's entire demeanor changed and lightened somewhat. He addressed the court room with an air of a master of ceremonies introducing a theatre act.

"Motions must be filed within fifteen days," his deep voice resonated with what seemed to be good grace and his arm made a sweeping motion while he carried on, "before a trial date can be set in the cases of David Thomas Riley and Leonard Malcolm Owen."

"Sir, may I approach the bench?" asked Alvin Goldberg, suited and booted in pinstripes and patent leather. Cooke nodded and the lawyer stepped forward. "The bonds for my clients have been set at $50,000 each. They cannot raise this. Would your honor consider lowering the sum so that Mr. Riley and Mr. Owen may be free to aid in the preparation of their defense?"

"Alright. The bond amount is reduced to $10,000 each," said Cooke, nodding. The room was filled with reactions of surprise. Judge Cooke made an irritated shushing sound and slammed down his gavel, keen to move on.

He then called upon Donovan Jones, 25, flanked by his two comrades, William Taylor, 22, and Alan Chase, 30. Judge Cooke asked why they were not represented by counsel and the latter both claimed to be destitute. The judge ordered his clerks to find a lawyer who could represent the accused men and asked if Taylor and Chase were ready to register a plea.

"Not guilty, your honor," they both muttered.

Cooke motioned for them to sit back down, which they did, leaving Jones standing. Jones was also asked how he wanted to plea and if he needed a court appointed lawyer, but Jones shook his head and said "no."

"No to which of my questions?" Cooke bellowed, making Jones jump.

"Both."

"Why do you not need a lawyer?" snapped Cooke.

"I claim the right to represent myself," Jones replied, his large bulk crammed into a blue shirt that was a size too small for him. The hairs on his chest peeped over the unbuttoned collar.

Cooke's eyebrows almost shot up into the depths of his receding hairline. "When it comes to the case of stealing your employer's shrimp boat on April 14, for the purpose of sailing it to Cuba in order to defect, how do you plead?"

"Guilty," announced Jones. The whole room was astounded to hear the ex-shrimper's reply

"Do you know the position such a plea puts you in?" Cooke was amazed.

"I do, your honor."

The judge went on to ask Jones why he was pleading guilty.

"My actions were honorable. It was not my intention to bring dishonor to myself or the United States Government."

Again, Cooke considered Jones, and with a distinct tinge of sarcasm in his voice, said, "Really. You had honorable intentions, Mr. Jones?"

"I can't say, sir," replied Jones. His bristled chin jutting forward proudly. Then he quickly looked at Cooke, whose lips were pinched in a tight line. Journalists in the public gallery grimaced at one another.

"Oh, you can't say," suppressing bubbling anger mused the judge.

"No disrespect, your honor," put in Jones nervously.

Cooke grunted, unimpressed and accepted Jones' plea, before sentencing him to two years imprisonment.

Hours later, on his way to a jail cell, Donovan Jones told a

Miami Herald reporter, "I just sincerely regret that I wasn't able to do in Cuba what I went there to do." When asked to clarify his statement, all Jones would say was, "I would say if I could, but I am not at liberty to do so."

No one ever found out what the three shrimpers' real intentions were when they sailed to Cuba that warm spring day in 1962.

David Thomas Riley and Leonard Malcolm Owen were once again made aware of the accusations against them. After presiding over the case, it was now Judge Emmet Cooke's turn to address the court room with his decision. He cleared his throat dramatically and looked across his packed courtroom. He then began his summation speech.

"What we're about to do here will set policy for the country for decades to come. We're dealing with two separate charges. One is kidnapping and the other is air piracy. You put the two together and we've got this newly emergent crime, covered by an equally new federal law that I must emphasize once more incurs the death penalty."

Judge Cooke referred to a law passed by Congress in 1961. Elected officials had taken action because similar incidents were on the up, yet until this moment no one had yet been charged with the crime of air piracy, much less been executed for it. So, Cooke's imminent decision was about to determine the viability of a new law Congress had attempted to put in place.

The judge continued, "Kidnapping involves a selfish motive, such as a ransom waiting at the end should the kidnapper succeed. However, nowhere in these documents here in front of me does it even suggest the accused wanted money in return for pilot Reginald Doan." Cooke then glared at Dave and Lenny waggling a stern index finger and snapped, "I am not saying that these two men were right or that this does not constitute a crime. All I'm saying is that their actions don't fit the crime of kidnapping—not in my view.

Let's move on to the charge of air piracy. The law requires for the crime of air piracy the action of the accused must involve air commerce. For example, stealing cargo from a seized vessel that has commercial value, in this case, the plane that had been hired to transport from one place to another. There was no freight aboard the Cessna that day, so this does not fit into the definition of air piracy."

He paused for reflection, scratched his head and then continued, "There is no evidence either that the accused had any desire to keep the Cessna for themselves or to sell it, so, therefore, it is my opinion that the crime of air piracy does not apply in this case."

Dave and Lenny looked at one another, open-mouthed. There were murmurs from the gallery until Assistant District Attorney Edmond Chang, assigned to prosecute the case, sprang from his seat. His face was trying to hide the disquiet he felt. He took a step forward.

"Umm, your honor," he said. "I move to dismiss the old charges."

Cooke simply eyed him suspiciously and then he raised an eyebrow that allowed the young man to carry on if he so wished.

Chang cleared his throat and smoothed down his spotted tie. "What I mean is that I'd like to take a few days to try to reword those charges, if you would allow, so they are more in fitting with the actual actions which the two accused took. I think there might have been some muddying of the waters here, your honor."

A smirk played across Cooke's lips. "I see..." He took a few moments to mull over the request. Immediately losing interest and gathering his papers in preparation to leave the court room he eventually said, "Fair enough. I will hear these charges on Wednesday."

With Cooke's hasty exit, the first day of the proceedings were at an end. Chang was adamant that this case was not going to be dropped, not if he had anything to do with it. He bustled out onto the street, barked a few determined words to the assorted press and jumped in his car, speeding off into the distance. But the hot-headed young prosecutor was soon to be disappointed when one month later David Thomas Riley and Leonard Malcolm Owen walked out of Dade County Federal Courthouse free men. They practically danced down the front steps, flanked by their overtly chipper lawyer, Alvin Goldberg. Dave pumped the hand of Goldberg, almost separating his shoulder joint from its socket, while the press gathered around shouting a barrage of questions.

"I knew we'd do it!" Riley told Goldberg over the noise. "

"We sure did, Dave, like you always said!" agreed Owen. "Let's go get a beer."

"You coming?" Dave asked Goldberg.

Goldberg shook his head, not one to socialize with clients. "I've got paperwork, but you two have one for me."

"Oh we will, Alvin, buddy, don't you worry," said Dave. "C'mon Lenny. Let's drink to freedom!" Goldberg smiled as he watched the duo disappear into the distance, Dave slapping Lenny on the back and laughing.

But the newspapers didn't back up Riley's buoyant mood. A *Miami Herald* story noted that although Judge Cooke had indeed allowed Riley and Owen to walk out of his courtroom, it also said their freedom "may not be for long."

Karl Wallen and other staff writers at the publication had witnessed Edmund Chang's attitude and knew very well that he was not the type to give up. Days later a headline read, "Two Men Re-Indicted in Skyjack." Dave and Lenny's barroom celebration had come too soon. This time, Riley's bravado was gone. The cockiness he and Owen projected a little more than a week earlier when Judge Cooke had set them free, replaced by frightened looks in their eyes.

"What do you think about the new indictment?" *Miami Herald* writer Carl Perkins called out from the swarm of reporters outside the court room. Riley simply shook his head and although he was secretly unnerved by the change in circumstances, he couldn't resist. Dave cracked his usual broad smile, basking in the media attention that meant so much to him.

"We consider it harassment," lawyer Goldberg almost shouted, indignation showing in the way his hand waved and his hair flopped onto his forehead.

"If you are innocent," another reporter asked Dave, "why Cuba?"

Goldberg leaned in close to Riley, still on the court steps, whispering in his ear that he ought to keep quiet.

"Yeah, Dave," said Lenny. "Keep it down. We don't wanna be speaking to these assholes." Lenny was about to give the media the finger, but Goldberg swatted his hand down telling Lenny to behave.

"Like I said," Riley explained, ignoring his lawyer's advice. "We were two honest American citizens taking pictures."

"How were you treated by the Cubans?" asked the reporter.

"Respectfully."

"And?"

"And what?" shrugged Dave, grinning. "Then they sent us back to Miami. We didn't even know until they dropped us at the airport."

"What did you think they were going to do with you?"

"We thought we were dead, until we got home. But when we got back someone informed us we were facing these charges. We couldn't believe it. We're patriotic Americans."

"So this is all a big mistake?" Carl Perkins asked, his face showing disbelief.

"Hey! Spot on, buddy boy!" Riley nodded, pointing at the *Herald* staff writer. "You ain't wrong there! Remember to put that in your story!"

"And fucking smoke it," mumbled Lenny, backing away a few steps, keen to escape the crowds.

Under renewed pressure from Edmund Chang and his cronies, Judge Cooke had little choice but to send Riley back into custody unless he could post bond now set for $25,000. Dave couldn't come up with the money, so was returned to jail, often spending time languishing in the CIA-run apartment on the prison grounds of Miami Dade County Jail, where his girlfriend Julie was permitted to join him for conjugal visits. During the many times he was let out to wander by the CIA, he was booked to carry out more missions to Cuba for them or simply allowed to do as he pleased. Dave spent countless nights at Julie's plush North Miami apartment, only to be quickly ordered back to jail by the Feds when a visit from his lawyer was scheduled. And more importantly for Dave, his pockets remained full for the time being.

Then the newspapers announced that pilot Reginald Doan would be called to testify. Dave's alarm didn't last very long as Judge Cooke dismissed, for a second time, all charges against the accused the following day. Chang felt like hitting his head against a wall, and hard. Dave was smugger than ever, suggesting to Lenny that they deserved a vacation in Las Vegas. So, once more, Dave, Lenny and their attorney Alvin Goldberg pranced delightedly down those courthouse steps, faces beaming nonchalantly for the press while Edmund Chang slipped away quietly, not wanting to be photographed by the news media. Chang could well have hoped that Riley might have had the good grace to not gloat on the occasion, but the spotlight proved too much for the self-styled celebrity, who had bought an expensive new tweed jacket for the glittering occasion. Dave pulled out his aviator sunglasses from his inside pocket, wiping the lenses first on his sleeve, before putting them in place. Lenny, as always, stood at his side, a serene smile playing on his lips.

"Are you a communist or socialist?" shouted out a female voice.

"Neither! C'mon lady," laughed Dave, flirting with the attractive brunette journalist and motioning at his attire. "Look at me. Do I look like a Commie?"

"What are you, then?"

Dave put his hand flat on his chest and pulled an earnest face, as if he were President Kennedy about to make a speech at the White House. "I am a loyal American. I'm a patriot. Socialism, to me, rates in degrees and I think our country tends to lean that way more so each year."

"So it's true then, as Judge Cooke ruled, you didn't kidnap Reginald Doan?"

"Uh-huh. Uh-huh. We told the pilot to circle Cuba so we could take photographs."

"What were these pictures for?" piped up another journalist, waving his hand so that Dave would spot him in the crowd.

"To see what was going on down there."

"You see yourself as a reporter, then?"

"Hey, you got it! I'm just like one of you guys, except of course, I'm freelance." Dave gave the impression that being freelance meant he was a cut above the full-time reporters huddling around him. Hardly a writer, the only time Dave, with his dyslexia, managed to put pen to paper was when he forged other people's signatures on checks.

The questioning continued, "Why did you land the Cessna?"

"You'd land too if you had a fuel shortage," shrugged Dave.

"Doan said you put a gun to his head."

Dave swiped off his shades and his expression was one of a mortally wounded man. "But I don't even own a gun."

THE SUPREME COURT ANNOUNCED it would review Chang's appeal to overturn Judge Cooke's second dismissal. When Judge Cooke, dismissed the indictment a second time, he had actually sniffed at the continuous pleadings of the federal prosecutor. Chang's argument that to throw out the case would free criminals on a technicality was a direct affront against Judge Cooke's court. Chang was about to give up the ghost for good when the highest court in the land took the appeal under consideration. The Justice Department was claiming that Judge Cooke's decision ran contrary to the intent of the lawmakers. Air piracy carrying the death penalty did apply here because the Cessna 172, which was allegedly skyjacked, had been for hire so it was considered air commerce. Also, the Cessna had flown through federal airway corridors at the time of the abduction, as such, it was considered a skyjacking under federal guidelines. As to the kidnapping accusation, the intent of the law was whenever a man puts a gun to another man's head and orders him to go somewhere against his wishes, the act is kidnapping, whether there is ransom or not. Dave was now quaking in his low-rent cowboy boots.

The Supreme Court's decision, which ordered a reopening of the skyjack case, renewed optimism in Chang. He rounded up his colleagues and announced that with a little luck, the Court would be wrapping everything up by November 22, 1963 before they all headed home for Thanksgiving. Miami lawyer Robert Shevin now represented Riley and explained his client's position during the oral-argument phase. Likewise, Chang had given way to a more experienced spokesman for the prosecution, Stephen J. Pollack, a heavy duty Justice Department lawyer. Both lawyers agreed and made it understood that the person really on trial here was not Riley, the defendant, but District Judge Emmet Cooke himself, who was deeply affronted by this new direction in the case.

Respect for Cooke's long-standing reputation was about to be challenged by the nine Justices of the Supreme Court through their decision to order a new trial. Washington lawmakers had worded the Air Piracy Law of 1961 in what they believed to be clear and simple language. Pollack argued Cooke's earlier decision to dismiss the case stood in stark disregard to the law in the books. Judge Cooke was not a happy man and made this point crystal clear in his attitude to the ongoing proceedings. He deemed the whole affair unjust.

WHILE THE COURT CASE carried on, another rather startling story hit the newspapers. On the morning of January 22, 1964, the *Miami Herald* reported "Two chain store employees, kidnapped Tuesday by a masked gunman, turned on him and beat him, but he escaped only to be caught 30 minutes later by the police." The holdup began at 8:30AM in a 7-Eleven store at Coral Way, Miami and ended near NW 45th Ave, where the accused bandit was found hiding neck-deep in a canal, the report said. "Booked on suspicion of robbery and kidnapping was David Thomas Riley, 25, of Obispo St., Coral Gables." Riley had stolen $2,000, plus 35 to 40 checks from the store. Nursing minor bruises from their tussle with Riley, the store manager, Willie Vails, 35, and a supervisor, Hassel Wright, 44 told the reporter that they were in the store when a man wearing a mask made of adhesive tape and gauze entered.

"He looked like he had been in an accident and had been bandaged," Wright said.

Dave had used a 38-caliber Belgian automatic to force Vails and Wright to open the safe and then he picked up a paper bag containing the money. Surprisingly, Vails and Wright were then ordered into the latter's car with Dave driving and the automatic in his lap. Vails was forced into the rear, while Wright was sitting in front.

"It was the weirdest thing to be riding with this man in the mask," Wright reflected. "He told us he was going to put us in the trunk." At that point the victims, each much taller than Riley, had had enough and realized they could easily overpower the rude interloper. Then Vails and Wright began to laugh at the man who had terrified them earlier. After a scuffle, Dave ran off and hid up to his neck in a nearby canal, until the cops found him and yanked him out, covered in weeds and slime.

Dave in the middle of the high profile Air Piracy case, couldn't resist the temptation of another exciting robbery. With anti-Castro funding down to virtually nothing, Riley was back to being a petty robber. But that would soon change with the Vietnam War heating up and the CIA's need for operatives for Air America operating in Southeast Asia.

ON JULY 17, 1964, more than two years since their first appearance before District Judge Emmet Cooke, David Thomas Riley and Leonard Malcolm Owen once more approached the bench. This time showing tired and depressed faces instead of cocky ones. With lawyers for the defendants by their sides, Cooke also noticeably downcast, once more dictated the pair of charges they faced, his voice sounding jaded, as if all this had become an annoying ritual and one he wanted to be rid of soon. The judge asked if they fully comprehended the seriousness of the situation, having been referred back to him by The Supreme Court of the United States, no less. Riley and Owen, now visibly afraid, nodded.

"The trial will commence August 10," sighed Cooke, who then abruptly stood and left the room. As Riley and Owen exited, courtroom reporters again crowded around hoping for a statement.

This time, Riley followed his lawyer's orders and remained quiet, leveling his eyes on the ground.

"You OK, Dave?" asked Lenny, not used to seeing his pal so down in the mouth.

Dave quickly smiled and slapped Lenny on the shoulder. "Hey man, no need to worry about me."

August came and went without a trial. And so did September and October. Dave grew restless. He was well aware that everything relied on what Reginald Doan would say when he took the stand. Here, the prosecution knew it held a winning card. Who would trust a criminal like Dave Riley over a clean-cut pilot? Riley was also a notorious con artist, as news reports had pointed out, highlighting his past arrest for the attempted extortion against respected county designer, Raymond Hooper, as well as his recently foiled 7-Eleven store robbery. Some were beginning to see Riley as a joke.

In early November '64, Judge Cooke and a 12-member jury sat observing as the U.S. Supreme Court ordered trial officially began. Two assistant U.S. Attorneys submitted a list of 13 government witnesses, including their prime guy, pilot Reginald Doan. The following day Doan took the stand, locking eyes with Judge Cooke for a moment, who appeared grumpy and washed out as he rummaged his pocket for a handkerchief. Doan spoke clearly and carefully when addressing the court, going over the whole skyjacking experience.

"Can you recall," attorney James Moore asked Doan, "any of the precise language used towards you during the flight to Cuba?"

"Yes. Once we were airborne, one of them told me I had to cooperate or get out and walk." Doan's earnest young face looked in the direction of Judge Cooke, who by this time was visibly distracted, polishing his glasses or shifting papers around just for the hell of it.

Moore however was on a roll and firing questions at the witness, "Once you approached the island, did Riley get more specific in his instructions?"

"Yes. He told me to head for Havana. But we missed the capital, so I had to land at Camp Libertad," said Doan, glancing at Cooke.

"How long did you remain there?"

"About two days. Then we were transported to Havana and were placed in El Principe prison for almost a week."

"What happened during that time?" queried Moore.

"I prayed I'd be sent back to America."

"What did the others do?"

"Riley and Owen sought asylum from Castro's government. As I begged to be returned to America, they pleaded with our captors not to be sent home," said Doan.

Another witness was then called, one of the shrimpers, Donovan Jones of Fort Myers stated the defendants told him they held a 38 caliber revolver at the pilot's head as they commandeered the plane. Jones, held captive with Reginald Doan in the Cuban prison, backed up Doan's kidnap story.

Leonard Owen soon took the stand in his own defense and during cross-examination insisted he had no idea why Doan would fabricate a skyjacking story. David Riley did not take the stand. Riley's attorney, Albert Saunders wanted a check on Riley's understanding of the charges against him. Saunders' appeal was favored by the opposition. The CIA considered Riley a walking time-bomb which could go off in court anytime, exposing the Agency's secret flights to Cuba program. Get him over to a shrink and out of the courtroom, both sides were saying.

Judge Cooke agreed a mental examination would be in the best interest of all, so Dave was sent to the office of psychiatrist James L. Anderson. Riley's defense lawyer knew he'd have cause for dismissal if Dr. Anderson would only find Riley didn't know reality from unreality, but the results came back "inconclusive." Saunders didn't push for further studies of Dave's mind.

Judge Cooke was not used to being overridden by Supreme Court of the United States. Court veterans noted Cooke's usual confidence had dissipated and he seemed thoroughly fed up. He felt betrayed and humiliated by the court system which had overruled him.

As he addressed the jury, Judge Cooke stared straight ahead with an empty look in his eyes. His shoulders hunched as he leaned his elbows on the bench, chin resting in his cupped hands. Journalists in the gallery couldn't help but feel sorry for this once highly respected judge, now enduring the most awkward and disappointing moment of his long judicial career.

All the while Riley and Owen sat stock still, waiting to learn whether the jury would find them innocent or guilty, and whether Cooke would impose the death penalty. Dave stared into space, his face hiding his emotions, while Lenny looked even more petrified than usual, standing there in his wonky tie and greasy hair that needed a good cut.

Albert Saunders, making a final desperate appeal, argued that the government's case ought to be considered inconsistent and therefore both men should be freed.

The judge would have none of it. He then held up a hand, "mandatory sentences are vicious." addressing the court in a resigned tone. "This is the most unfair law I have ever encountered. Most countries don't give you 20 years for murder. Mandatory sentences should not be imposed by Congress."

The jury deliberated for four hours before returning to the courtroom with the foreman announcing they had reached a verdict. David Thomas Riley and Leonard Malcolm Owen were found guilty of both charges of Air Piracy and Kidnapping. On November 13, 1964, Judge Cooke sentenced Owen and Riley to the minimum 20 years, the two sentences to run concurrently. He looked apologetically towards Riley and Owen, hands clasped behind their backs.

"It's the opinion of this court," Judge Cooke said, "that the sentence of 20 years in your case is crueler than the old sentence to kill a starving man for stealing a loaf of bread. But the court is powerless because the law says that I must hold to the mandatory sentence that has been set by Congress in their skyjacking statute."

Riley and Owen stared helplessly at the floor as they were led away. But as the courts had written their final chapter, there were a couple of unnoticed clauses stating "unless excused earlier by the warden," and "the appellant would be eligible for parole at any such time the Board of Parole might determine."

FOURTEEN

"HEY, MARCELLO! LONG TIME no see!" Dave said as he strolled into his favorite barber shop in downtown Miami, slapped the proprietor on the shoulder and sat in a swivel chair, ready for his haircut. He placed a couple of plastic bags with new clothes in down by his side.

"Davy boy, ain't seen you for ages!" Marcello, a fat bald guy in his late 60s, smiled and wiped a comb on his white apron before he slid a razor across the back of a customer's head with great care. "You sit. Be with you in a minute."

"I've been on important business. You know how it is. Keeping the Feds sweet and all that…" Dave smiled knowingly at Marcello, an eyebrow hoisted, but the older guy passed him back a blank look. He wasn't one for keeping up with the news and so far Dave's recent fame hadn't made its presence felt in his tiny linoleum-floored emporium with its half-lit neon sign hung above the door. Dave picked up the rumpled paper on the shelf in front of him and shook it out in order to read. He shrugged. "Hey, no hurry, Marcy. Whenever you're ready."

It wasn't clear just how many weeks, days or hours Dave and Lenny spent in Miami Dade County jail for the air piracy and kidnapping offenses, but before anyone could mutter the words CIA, Riley was back out on the streets and up to his old tricks. First things first though, he needed to sort out his appearance. Prison and heated court battles did little for the kind of image he liked to maintain and he had a hot date lined up later, now that Julie was no longer on the scene. So Dave did some shopping and popped into his favorite barber's to get his flat top trimmed.

Lenny, on the other hand, decided to keep his head down for a while with all the fuss surrounding the case. He had enough excitement to last a lifetime so he spent his days hanging out on the beach or with an array of different women he picked up in the nearby bars, many of whom were in Miami on vacation or just passing through. Like his buddy, he had no fixed abode and wandered from one one-night-stand to the next, eking out his welcome in random females' motels or apartments, drinking beer, gambling and scraping a living.

There was no announcement about Dave and Lenny's release and no press conference. The Feds relied heavily on the hope that the furor would be forgotten and the case would simply die a quiet death and everyone would forget about Riley and Owen. Slowly but surely everything had indeed returned to normal and Dave Riley was going about his business as if the famous *Black Friday* case was just a dim and distant memory.

But to one man the whole affair was far from forgotten. Edmund Chang was livid when he found Dave and Lenny had been seen out and about. He called a news conference demanding to know.

"What's going on at Dade County Jail?" he shouted before attending reporters.

The Feds replied "Oh they must have been out cutting grass. We just lost track of where they were within the compound." Immediately and secretly, Dave and Lenny were ordered back to jail. The cover worked, but until things quieted down again they were locked-in 24/7.

The prosecutor kept a closer eye on them for a while, but Chang never learned of Dave's special treatment within the jail, the private apartment and permission to receive guests. And few knew they weren't actually doing the 20-year stretch that Judge Cooke had been forced to hand down.

The Feds were watching and using Riley when Lenny pulled a surprise. With the ever-present shadow of the *Black Friday* case looming over his shoulder, and the possibility of being returned to prison to serve out the full 20-year sentence was too much of a risk for Lenny so he split for Canada. Dave's partner in crime got the idea of Canada while watching a late night TV show, which said women in certain regions of Canada were desperate for husbands and there were plenty of high paying labor-intensive jobs for which he could qualify. Owen was lonely and broke, so he packed a bag with a change of clothes, tucked his passport in the back pocket of his Levis and got on a flight at Miami International Airport to Vancouver. To his shock and disappointment, the women of Canada weren't so desperate that they were willing to take on an undereducated, scruffy ex-con with no money and no career prospects. After nearly three years of bumming around Canada, Lenny grew homesick, thinking it was time to return to his roots. Perhaps he missed his best friend, Dave.

In the fall of 1968, he was caught by the police at a Maine-Canadian border station. Back to prison he went for skipping the country, a serious parole violation. The courts had it on record that he had not served his time for the air piracy and kidnapping offenses before his disappearing act. Now the Feds weren't interested in helping Dave Riley's elusive ex-sidekick anymore. They left Lenny to his own fate. His attorney argued that his client hadn't been in court while an appeal against his 20-year sentence had been considered, but this was later turned down. Lenny had been living in a cheap boarding house in Strathcona, Vancouver, at the time, so it was his lawyer's tenuous argument that it was unfair to now jail him without the appeal process taking place again. The court didn't see why his not being present during the original proceedings made any difference to Owen's current situation and cited many cases where the defendant wasn't in court during their appeal hearings. Lenny was back in jail. When he was released five years later he kept his nose clean and retired from the criminal world. He didn't look up Dave and they never saw one another again.

Dave, on the other hand, had been busy carrying out various store holdups during the mid 60s to early 70s and was dabbling in other crime, somehow managing to evade arrest, in between making CIA connections in Southeast Asia during the Vietnam War with Air America.

Air America, the United States civilian airline operated by the CIA during the Vietnam War, played a major part in supplying guns and drugs to the KMT (Kuomingtang) troops in the Golden Triangle, the world's drug center where Burma (later called Myanmar,) Laos and Cambodia converge. In 1968-1969, CIA assets were used, opening a generous cluster of heroin laboratories for the Golden Triangle. KMT General Tuan Shi-Wen explained "To fight communists you must have an army, an army must have guns and to buy guns you must have money. In these mountains, the money is opium and this currency is traded for food, clothing and utensils."

So, the CIA had inadvertently become a drug dealer to stop the communists from moving south into Thailand. Operatives helped supply KMT with weapons and copious amounts of drugs. When the Laotian Army commander opened a heroin laboratory to supply drugs to U.S. troops in Vietnam, the Agency remained silent. By 1971, a white paper study indicated 34% of U.S. troops stationed in Vietnam were addicted to heroin.

Dave could now see where his future lay. Hard drugs meant hard cash in his pocket for life. When he came back to Miami, Dave intended to find a way in which to use his vast drug knowledge on home turf. Meantime, he still dabbled in lowlier levels of crime for excitement and pin money. Seeing himself as some kind of a CIA-backed gun-toting drug baron with extraordinary contacts and power, his confidence soared to even more alarming levels. And in September 1972, he was busy planning yet another holdup while staying with a stripper named Patsy he had met in a local underground club. As long as he wasn't caught and in the papers, the Feds were happy to just let him do his thing, as long as he kept his bargain of not exposing where the Feds were getting some of their operative recruits. He was extremely useful on the outside informing the police, FBI and ATF on other criminals. Somehow he managed to escape detection when he was ratting on his brothers in crime. Living through the dangers of Southeast Asia, he enjoyed big pay. Back home, the CIA was still suffering from punishing financial cutbacks handed the Agency by the late Kennedy Brothers for the failed *Bay of Pigs* invasion.

Always out of money, which hardly had a chance to slide down the lining of his trouser pockets before it was spent, Dave hoped his next holdup would be more lucrative than his last. He had scoped out Tate's Pharmacy on NW 42nd Avenue, Miami, for his next heist. He tightened up the logistics before he made his move, to be certain he couldn't be caught. It made him proud that he had outsmarted the cops in all of his felonious activities but one, the failed 7-Eleven store heist back in January 1964. The humiliating capture by police who caught him hiding neck deep in a local canal, he had been omitted from his memory bank. As far as Dave was concerned, he had gotten away with a bigger and better crime in '64 and if he could outwit the highest court in the land and that tenacious Assistant District Attorney Edmond Chang, then he must be infallible. After all, the Feds had seen to it that they still had one of their favorite criminal operatives on hand to carry out missions to Cuba, Vietnam or wherever else they felt like sending him. Having supported the rulings of Judge Cooke in 1964, "for the good of the country" they intimated, the CIA kept Riley out of jail.

Dave so confident in the protection the Agency afforded him, he bragged to anyone who cared to listen about his work with the CIA and how he was in essence above the law. Shop assistants, bartenders, neighbors and his many women were often regaled by Dave's secret spy stories. While other people grew sick of hearing about what they wrongly assumed was complete bull, Riley never tired of talking about his greatness.

Dave realized that his petty crimes weren't enough to keep him afloat. So, while edging towards his mid-thirties, he resorted to scrounging from his mom for money again.

Dave's four brothers tried avoiding their embarrassment of a sibling more than ever. Infuriated when he turned up at the family home with his hand outstretched. Dave's mother Mary would still dip her hand in her purse for a small wad of dollar bills to give him, while reminding the family, "David is a good boy, really. He just gets mislead by others." The men in the family were fully aware just how deluded Mary was when it came to her youngest boy and her husband Patrick despaired with her naiveté.

"For God's sake, Mary. The boy's no good. Stop giving him our hard earned money!" he told her, but she refused to listen, even offering to wash and iron Dave's laundry on a weekly basis. Patrick Riley would leave the room, his head shaking with disgust at his wife's inability to see the truth. He thanked the Lord for his other four sons. To him, they were enough and he had come to the conclusion that David was just the bad apple in an otherwise outstanding barrel. Patrick was of course disappointed that, in his view, his youngest son didn't have a decent, law abiding bone in his body, but he reasoned that he had done well with the others, all whom had good jobs and were married with kids. He thanked the Lord above for small mercies.

ON OCTOBER 12, 1972, Arnold Markoff, a *Miami Herald* staff writer wrote, "David T Riley, who was kicked out of Cuba for hijacking an airplane in 1962, has been arrested and charged with the armed robbery of a Miami drugstore." The report went on to mention the *Black Friday* case ten years prior and how Riley had served three years in jail for the offense. No one, including the press, was suspicious Dave had been enjoying so much freedom during that period. The article continued, "In addition, Riley, 33, faces a possible return to federal prison to serve out the rest of a 20-year prison sentence for air piracy. Riley was arrested on Tuesday night by Detective Charles Hines of the Miami Police robbery squad, following an 11-day investigation."

On September 29, Dave had entered Tate's Pharmacy store with a pistol and while waving the weapon at staff, wearing a mask fashioned from a plastic wrapping with cutouts for eye and mouth holes, he had ordered them to hand over a supply of drugs, four cartons of cigarettes and $150 in cash. It hardly seemed worth the trouble. Now he had been caught and was back in Dade County Jail in a prison issue jumpsuit. His run of good luck had temporarily ended, again.

In a few days, Dave was out of jail and back on the loose again, with a busty casino croupier named Tracey-Jane on his arm. He had money in his pocket from a recent job he had carried out for the CIA, which saw him make a return to Cuba on another mission. It had been a success, but the Feds still weren't using him as much as he would have liked and cash wasn't rolling in, so Dave had been observing the daily routines of the staff at another local store, with a hold up in mind. Store checks and cartons of stolen cigarettes were just pocket money though. He wanted big bucks and he aimed to find a way of getting it.

On a piping hot day in May 1978, Dave accidentally stumbled upon the biggest earning opportunity of his entire life. Little did he know that he was about to hit pay dirt, which to him, would be a better prospect than being a rock 'n' roll star. He hadn't given up on his singing dreams entirely, but he was aware that at 38 he needed to have a back-up plan.

He and his new girlfriend Sandra needed somewhere to stay for the night so she parked her car on Biscayne Boulevard, Miami, in a lot of a large attractive building surrounded by palm trees. She and Dave got out and walked into the motel's office, where the owner, a well-groomed woman in her mid-fifties, wearing flared trousers and a polyester shirt, gave them a welcoming smile, just like she did for all of her guests.

JoAnne Novak was used to the comings and goings of random people and she didn't think much about Riley and his lady friend when she first set eyes on them. She noticed that he was smartly dressed in light slacks and shirt and the young woman at his side was dolled up to the nines in a skirt that barely covered her backside and wore too much mascara. JoAnne wondered briefly if the pair were married, but then doubted it. They didn't look the wedded-bliss type. It was of no consequence to JoAnne. She was a modern business woman.

She handed Dave the keys for room number 64 and asked, "How long are you planning to stay?"

"Just tonight," Dave shrugged and took a good long look at his new surroundings. "Maybe longer."

"Enjoy your stay," JoAnne smiled.

"We will, thanks," replied Dave, putting his arm around his girlfriend and making his way toward the office exit, where the rooms were situated.

JoAnne Novak wrote Dave Riley's name in the motel log,

below to all the other patrons that were listed in the large book. Unfortunately for her, it wouldn't be the last time he would stay. JoAnne hadn't bargained on how much her newest guest enjoyed motel hospitality. He was about to put his CIA education in the lucrative business of hard narcotics to the test and launch his own drug empire.

—Dave had just found the perfect venue.

FIFTEEN

J OANNE NOVAK WENT INTO the motel business twenty
months before Dave wandered onto the premises asking for a
room. On September 9, 1976, she excitedly signed on the dotted
line and bought the Biscayne Plaza Motel for $180,000. Some
might have called it a hotel, but in the busy location of Biscayne
Boulevard, 80 blocks north of the center of Miami, it was referred
to as a motel. JoAnne had worked as a beautician most of her
adult life, so becoming a Miami motel owner was a significant
shift in lifestyle, but one she was keen to make. As she headed
closer to retirement age, she proudly found herself the owner of an
expansive motel with a swimming pool, in a prime spot of bustling
Miami.

Born in 1920 and raised during the Depression, JoAnne learned
to never spend money on frivolous things and managed to save a
fair portion of her wages over the years. She was the eldest of four,
with a sister and two brothers. It was a happy childhood and she
and her mother were close. Her parents were hard working Polish
immigrants and had been business people when Jo and her siblings

grew up in South River, New Jersey. All four children did well at school and Jo went to college.

Afterwards, a local boy named Gary Novak noticed Jo about town and pursued her for a year or so, before he went away to serve in the Navy and while back home on-leave. An attractive dark-haired young woman, JoAnne had caught his eye and he was determined to make her notice him, although this was easier said than done. Gary was not all that much to look at and a few inches shorter than her willowy 5 feet 9 inches. Jo, while not enamored by this young man's interest at first, but gave in to his advances and married him in 1946.

He was a local South River, New Jersey, boy from a average family, with basic aspirations and Jo's respect for him waned a little over their 23-year marriage. She was a busy, working mother and focused on the upbringing of her two kids, Ben and Katherine. As Gary got older, JoAnne found herself spending more time warning her husband about his considerable weight gain. He had once been a slim man, but as he advanced further into middle age he became obese. Gary didn't heed her warnings and he died of a heart attack in his mid-fifties, while son Ben was in college. From then forward, JoAnne concentrated on being a mother and her career as a beautician, until she set out on her Miami motel venture.

Kobe, JoAnne's younger brother, was divorced from his wife Cindy in the late 60s. He left his job in a paper factory in July of 1976 in South River to assist JoAnne in the Miami business. She was close to her brother and had seen him go through some tough times over the years. As a 17-year-old, Kobe had demanded that his father sign the papers that would let him join the Navy during

World War II. He eventually relented and signed the document after his son threatened to forge his name. During the Battle of Leyte Gulf in 1944, in the eastern Philippines, Kobe sustained a serious hit on the head and was never the same after that. Although Kobe was on board at the motel, Jo remained the boss and was responsible for most of the big decisions and the day-to-day running of the establishment.

AFTER BOOKING IN FOR a few days with his latest girlfriend, Dave Riley had made it his number one priority to speak to JoAnne as much as possible. He had noticed the stars and stripes coffee mug on her desk and the way in which Jo presented herself, upright and proud. Dave had found something that he and this lady motel owner had in common, a hook that he could use.

"Hey, JoAnne. You don't mind me calling you that, do you?" Dave was loitering in the entrance to her office one afternoon.

JoAnne looked up from the paperwork on her desk and shook her head, "No, I guess not."

He was keen to make a good impression on her and win her over. In his opinion, he had a special way with women.

Dave moved towards her and closed the door a fraction behind him. "Um, I think you should know, um, I'm an agent on important federal business," he whispered, taking a few more steps into the small white-walled office and sitting on the edge of her desk. He leaned forward and glanced around him, as if someone might be listening in. "This is between you and me though, Jo. Do you prefer JoAnne or Jo?"

"I don't mind," she shrugged, wishing he would go so she could get on with her paperwork.

"I trust you, you know?" he carried on. "I can see that you're a real all-American patriot, like me." Dave placed the flat of his hand on his chest and flashed what he considered to be one of his winning smiles. "If ever you need anything, let me know. I have important, top secret contacts."

"Thanks," said Jo, nodding briskly.

Dave knew it was against the law to impersonate a law officer. If he was caught, it carried stiff penalties, so to say outright that he was a CIA agent was too much of a risk, even for him. Dave carried on dropping clues over the following days and weeks in order for JoAnne to get the message loud and clear.

Jo was no dummy, but it wasn't everyday that she had a government secret agent staying at her motel. Eventually, her initial business-like approach thawed. She was pleased to offer such an upstanding citizen a roof over his head, for nothing, for a short while. After Dave had gone into even more detailed speeches about dangerous missions abroad and how she too might help fight against the evils of world communism, Jo felt it was her civic duty to assist him.

Riley was soon living in room 64, permanently. Then he went about moving in his buddies, drug dealers, gunrunners, thieves, counterfeiters, and other criminals, until they filled the top floor. His drug empire was growing at a rate that even surprised him. He was dealing in tens-of-thousands of dollars worth of heroin a week and was also growing marijuana on the roof, two stories up in ten big pots, so it wasn't visible from busy Biscayne Boulevard below. Dave realized he needed security around him, so employed a massively-built guy named Lance who had an attitude as bad as his dress sense. Attired in a cheap suit and flowery shirt, Lance stood guard outside Dave's room every night, keeping a look-out while Dave slept, ensuring that no one encroached on his territory or tried to kill him.

One day Kobe went to his sister's motel room where she slept, barged in and shut the door behind him. His light brown hair wasn't even brushed yet. He was in such a hurry to speak to JoAnne. It was early in the morning and she was still in her night clothes.

"Jo, listen to me. You've got to get this Riley guy out. Something's not right."

"Don't be silly," scoffed JoAnne. "He works for the government. He told me."

"I'm warning you. Something funny's going on around here. Get him out or you'll have no business left," interrupted Kobe.

"Don't be so dramatic," sighed Jo.

"Don't say I didn't warn you. This guy is bad news."

"Kobe, it's early. I've got a lot to do today," sighed Jo.

"I'm worried." Although at least three inches taller and much broader than Riley, Kobe found his presence unnerving.

"Don't be," said Jo. "Everything's fine."

Dave's insistence on confiding in JoAnne about dangerous missions and people being killed or turning up dead kept her in a permanent state of edginess and confusion. She had heard what Kobe was saying, but it wasn't sinking in properly. Riley was working his magic, drip-feeding information to keep her in a state of permanent insecurity.

"It's so good to have someone decent like you on my side, you know," Dave never tired of telling her.

Jo didn't know what to believe.

Just as spring was becoming summer in 1978, Dave felt the time was ripe to up his game. Dave needed a significant injection of cash-flow for his heroin operation. He approached JoAnne in her office one day.

"Hey, Jo, I got a group of top federal agents visiting in a few weeks for secret business meetings and we need $20,000 to get this place looking just right. These fellas are real top notch guys, y'know. You don't know how lucky you are to be picked specially."

Dave was wearing a slick new suit and his favorite aviator shades nestled in his front pocket. Jo's face paled at his request. She had sunk all of her life savings into the motel purchase and couldn't lay her hands on a sum of that size. But she had noticed that Dave spent a lot of time in the Italian restaurant called Capra's opposite her motel, with a married couple called Lily and Tony Antonelli and various, unfriendly-looking men of Latin description. Everyone in the area knew they were Mafia. Frank Sinatra ate at the place when he performed on Miami Beach. Starstruck, Riley was constantly telling people this fact. Not only was Dave impressed by Sinatra's music, but he loved the fact that his hero had an affiliation with the Mob.

JoAnne didn't like Dave. She never did. But she worried about what he or one of the people with him might do to her or her family if she didn't give him the money. JoAnne vividly recalled an incident that underlined why she let Dave into her life. When she was starting out on her career as a beautician, JoAnne, then in her 20s, attended a convention not too far from her parents store in New Jersey. Afterwards she drove home to her apartment, where she received a panicked phone call from a neighbor of her parents, saying that her parents' store was on fire. As quick as she could, she located her parents, told them about the fire and they all raced to the store, where they found the room at the back of the building engulfed in flames.

This was a large room where her mom and dad kept goods like clothes and shoes. Not long before, the local Mafia had asked to use the space, as they wanted to license it and run it as a late night drinking club, but Jo's father declined. The family didn't want their respectable business tainted by the Mob. Now, it had all gone up in smoke. Luckily though, fire fighters saved the front of the three-story structure, but there was considerable damage to the large back room. The fire left it ruins. The Mob made sure no one else would get it either.

JoAnne had watched the comings and goings from Capra's with growing alarm. She saw how a constant stream of characters would exit the eatery and then make their way to the top floor of her motel. Remembering the fire at her parent's store, she put two and two together.

Worried about rejecting Dave's request for money, she turned to her sister Halena Marek who handed her $20,000 for the renovations. The siblings were always supportive of one another, but Halena warned her sister that she would need the $20,000 repaid so she could buy a spring collection for her own dry goods store on a property next to her father's property in New Jersey.

Meanwhile, Dave brought his crooked lawyer friend Nathan Lomax on board to snoop into JoAnne's business. Lomax was on her case at once discovering Jo's aunt, Julia Petrik, died in September 1978 leaving a $24,000 savings account to her niece.

"I don't know, David." JoAnne was walking quickly towards her car parked outside and keen to get away from Dave, who was trailing behind her. It was the third time in a week he had begged her for the money. He had a desperate edginess about him now and she was getting scared.

Dave suddenly pitched forward and grabbed Jo's arm, stopping her in her tracks. He looked at the ground and then back at her.

"Look, Jo, JoAnne, here's how it is, let me explain it properly." Dave thought for a long moment. "If you sign over the money to us, just think how impressed the President will be when I tell him!" He cajoled. "And we can put some of it towards the renovations for the big agents' arrival. Wow, what an opportunity! How can you possibly say no to the President?"

Eventually, JoAnne took out her checkbook, put her signature on the slip of paper and handed it to Dave. Over the following weeks she waited for the motel renovations to begin.

"I'm looking for the right interior design company," said Dave when she asked what was going on. "This place has to look just right. No point in rushing perfection."

"When are the agents coming?" asked JoAnne.

"They've been held up. They're real busy fighting communists," said Dave.

After JoAnne handed over both her sister's loan money and the cash from her deceased aunt's life savings account, Dave and Nathan Lomax were able to invest the cash in their various schemes. Lomax was a serious con artist, with an office above a closed-down store on Bird Road, 10 miles south of downtown Miami. Lomax, 43, was of the opinion that he was a hot shot respected businessman and a great catch for any woman. In reality, he was a rodent-faced guy, with fuzzy red sideburns and had an air about him that screamed crack-alley pimp. Lomax wasn't so big on personal hygiene either. In the summer, people would find him behind his desk, sweat stains decorating the front of his nylon shirt simply because he couldn't be bothered to open the window. Lomax was a perfect partner for Dave Riley's numerous rip-off schemes.

It wasn't long after Dave's move-in that JoAnne's brother, Kobe, discovered his precious coin collection was missing. At once, he knew who had taken it. He considered confronting Dave, but then thought better of it, knowing that Dave would never own up to it. Furious, Kobe got in his car and sped off to the cops to report the theft.

As Kobe was walking back into the motel, Dave dragged him to a quiet corner by the front of his shirt, pinned him to a wall and warned him.

"Don't do that again, buddy, or else."

Kobe wriggled in Dave's grasp. He was a sturdier build than Riley, but physical confrontation wasn't in his nature. "Let go!"

Dave pushed his smiling face into Kobe's. "Did you hear me, bud?"

"Yes, I heard you!" cried Kobe.

"Huh?"

"I hear you!"

"Good. You say one more word about me to the cops and you'll be sorry." Dave loosened his grip and smoothed down the front of Kobe's shirt. "I don't like squealers."

Riley had friends and informants everywhere, even in the Miami Police Department. Kobe wasn't stupid. He kept his head down. But, this wasn't enough for Riley. Dave wanted JoAnne's little brother gone, so he drafted in Elvis, another one of his sidekicks, to help out.

Riley trusted Elvis, having trained him himself. Elvis was no ordinary right hand-man, he was actually a green and yellow talking parrot. Elvis was the official look out for Dave's drug and gunrunning operations and he was good at his job. When there was a pick up or drop-off, he was always there on guard. If there was any sign of a cop or a curb-crawling squad car checking out the vicinity for pimps, prostitutes and dealers, Elvis squawked "Cops! Run!" and Dave was out of there in a flash.

In July 1978, Dave persuaded Kobe to carry out an assignment. He needed him to deliver a package to New Jersey and asked Kobe to take along Elvis.

"It's a vital federal mission, bud," said Dave.

It is unclear whether Elvis himself was the package to be delivered, if Dave gave Kobe a parcel to hand over to someone, or if it was simply a wild-goose chase for Riley to be rid of him for a while. When Kobe returned, along with Elvis, Dave assured Kobe that he was no danger to JoAnne.

"She's like my own sister, Kobe. I'll always look out for her. I promise." With his hand on his heart, "I'd die for her."

"I don't know?" Kobe was still not convinced.

"Hey, no bull," said Dave.

Although worried about JoAnne, Kobe's thoughts were on getting back with his ex-wife Cindy and daughter Amanda living in Tampa. He left and didn't intend to return to Miami.

—JoAnne was on her own. Just as Riley planned it.

SIXTEEN

B Y THE FALL OF 1978, Dave had not only persuaded JoAnne to hand over her Aunt Julia's $24,000 life savings, but he and his lawyer also arranged for the sale of the deceased woman's condo on Rodman Street in Hollywood. The deal was quick. Paperwork was processed by Lomax and the property was sold through real estate broker Frank Moby, listed as "The Best Bail Bondsman" on NW 14th Avenue in Miami.

JoAnne never saw a penny from the real estate transaction and immediately after the condo sold, Moby's business partner turned up dead in Georgia by a single shot to the head. No one was ever charged, but the murder scene had Riley's signature all over it.

Following the sale of Julia Petrik's condo, Riley approached Jo in the motel corridor with another idea.

"We need more money, Jo. Those commie's are tough nuts to crack," he said.

Jo was wrung out financially and emotionally. "I can't do anything else for you. I'm sorry." She went to walk away, but Dave blocked her path.

"Your Aunt Julia, she had Social Security, right?"

JoAnne had stopped wondering how Dave always managed to find out her business, even though it made her uneasy. "Yes, why?"

"We can still collect the checks," Dave said.

"But she's dead. She can't sign," Jo replied.

"She can't, but I can."

"I don't get it."

Dave sighed. Jo wasn't catching on quick enough, but he flashed her a smile. "If we pretend Aunt Julia is still alive, we can sign the checks and collect the money."

Jo's chin nearly hit the floor. "But that's illegal!"

Dave put his hand on her shoulder and leaned in close, "Not really. I work for some people high up in the governement. It's all for the cause. You'll be doing us a good turn."

JoAnne was appalled by Riley's suggestion, but he talked her into it, maintaining the money would be put to proper use. Jo didn't have the energy to ask any more questions. She just wanted to run her business.

A steady stream of criminals continued to moved into the motel. Local pimps and hoods had made it their home and prostitutes could be seen wandering the hallways in a heroin-induced daze. They were like parasites and JoAnne didn't have a clue of how to get rid of them. Worse yet, she also couldn't afford to pay back her sister Halena the $20,000 she borrowed to give to Riley and now Halena's store in New Jersey was in trouble.

TO KEEP HIMSELF OUT of jail for any one of his numerous offenses, Dave struck a deal. He ratted on local criminals in return for an exemption pass from doing time in Miami Dade County Jail. Not only was he a valuable assest to the CIA, but Dave managed to work his magic on the FBI, ATF and Miami Police too. It didn't take law enforcement long to realize that Riley would squeal on his own mother if it meant he'd be kept out of jail. They were bringing in local drug dealers and gunrunners faster than they could find the time to fill out each case's accompanying paperwork.

During those days, a chubby gunrunner named Freddie Short was always in Riley's company. He was one of those characters whose distinct lack of height only added to his nasty disposition. Freddie Short wore polyester suits and had a voice that could cut through a wall. When parading around the motel pool, he'd take every opportunity to swing his jacket open, to show everyone he was packing a weapon. He and his wife stayed in one of the rooms on the top floor and their bitter fights could often be heard echoing down the hall.

Dave had an intense dislike for Freddie referring to him as that "little fat freak" when he was out of earshot. But, Dave wasn't picky with whom he did business. He and Short were bringing in a mountain of money and Dave had also roped JoAnne into unwittingly helping with the racket too. He'd often got her to drive him to the Shooting Shack, the local weapons store where he would routinely pick up more guns and ammunition for Short to sell to his numerous contacts.

"Hey, Dave we got some business to see to at the Shack this afternoon," Short said to Dave as he lounged on the unmade double bed in room 64, the headquarters of Dave's empire. The floor was so littered with empty beer cans and takeaway cartons the carpet was barely visible.

"OK, I'll get Jo to run us down there," said Dave.

"I'm gonna get me a dumb broad to drive me around all day!" Short let out a deafening cackle. "My old lady don't even know how to drive in a straight line, the dumb fucking useless bitch!"

"Yeah, whatever," said Dave, trying to ignore Short's ramblings.

JUST A BLOCK FROM Biscayne Boulevard, on bustling 79th Street was a dentist's office, run by Dr. Erwin Rosen. Dave was getting Jo to run him there on a regular schedule.

"How long will you be?" Jo asked as she parked outside. She was getting tired of being at Dave's beck and call.

"Keep the engine running. I won't be long," he said and ducked out of the car.

"I can't wait too long! I've got dry cleaning to pick up!" Jo called out of the open driver's window, but Dave wasn't listening. JoAnne watched while he sprinted into the entrance of the building. She assumed he was on government business.

A bald man in late middle-age, Dr. Rosen stopped drilling teeth of one of his patients when the receptionist told him Dave was waiting to speak to him. He followed the girl into the nearly empty waiting room where Riley was waiting. Rosen didn't look happy and fortunately for him he didn't have many patients booked that day either.

"I told you to come after business hours," Rosen whispered to Dave. "This is most irregular."

"Yeah I know, but I need the stuff now," Dave hissed, motioning his head to the little office to the side of the waiting room.

"OK, but this mustn't happen again," Rosen said as he and

Riley stepped inside and shut the door. "I have to protect my reputation."

"The quicker you give me the stuff, the quicker I'll be out of your hair," said Riley. Since Rosen was bald, Dave hooted with laughter. "No offense."

Dentists, authorized to prescribe narcotics to their patients, were often sought out by cons like Riley, who was heavily engaged in the illegal diversion of pharmaceutical-quality drugs to the street market. There was only a minimal risk of arrest and conviction for the dealer, but such practices posed a much greater risk for professionals. Rosen wasn't the type you'd expect to get involved with the likes of Riley, but his appreciation for the finer things in life meant he couldn't turn down the extra income. After Dave left that day, he promised himself he would no longer do business with criminals. That evening, as he was locking up the office, someone edged out from the shadows.

"Dr. Erwin Rosen?" said the man.

Rosen spun around and swallowed hard. "Ah...Yes?"

"I've got a few questions to ask you down at the station," said the detective.

Rosen's dentist's license was lifted for the illegal dispensing of drugs to David Thomas Riley.

CARL MARCHETTI, A RETIRED New York City police detective, who was working as an American Express detective in the late 1970s, uncovered a Travelers' Cheques scheme run by Dave, whereby dozens of two-bit crooks, pretending to be tourists would spend the money and then go to American

Express offices, claiming their checks had been lost or stolen. The American Express office in Nassau, Bahamas, in particular, would immediately reimburse the phony tourists, before the then painfully slow computers could register back in Miami. Dave struck a deal with Marchetti, ratting on 15 of his mules, most of whom went to jail for a few months.

On the day of their release, Dave arranged a welcome home party. It was Christmas time and Dave laid out an enormous spread of delicacies and fine liquors for buddies' hard work. The motel's pool had been encircled with Christmas trees twinkling with tiny lights and garlands were draped on the outside walls of the motel and a local jazz band, accompanied by a singer who thought he was Frank Sinatra incarnate was hired. The grand shindig was financed by the sale of Jo's aunt's Hollywood condo.

Hours before the guests arrived, Dave strolled about the grounds of JoAnne's motel, a tumbler of bourbon in hand and his huge bodyguard, Lance, at his side.

"Hey, no one can say I don't look after my friends!"

"It sure looks pretty," whistled Lance.

At 8PM, men in evening suits and women in cocktail dresses made their way to the party, where Dave acted as gracious host, filling up champagne flutes from a magnum and offering the men cigars.

"Hey welcome home from the slammer everyone!" cried Dave as he mingled amongst his crooks.

"Hey, man, nice threads!" bellowed Freddie Short when he spotted Riley.

Dave grimaced when he saw Short skirt the edge of the pool and head in his direction. The fat guy was staggering and obviously already half-wasted. Dave painted on a smile as Short drew closer.

"Hey, thanks, Freddie," he said loudly and pointed at his shoes. "Handcrafted in Florence, these babies!"

He then spent the evening weaving in and out of groups of people, being the perfect host and ordering waitresses to take around more trays of canapés for his guests. When it hit 11PM, Dave asked the band to be silent and he got up on a little podium to make a speech.

"Friends, colleagues, business associates, everyone, this party is to say thank you and to welcome you home. I'd also like to extend an extra special thanks to the staff at Miami Dade County Jail for letting you all out in time for Christmas!"

Laughter and applause erupted and everyone agreed that the party was one of the best Miami had ever seen. As Dave's guests began to make their way home just before dawn, each thanked him for his generosity. Little did any of the revelers know, it was Dave who had landed them in jail in the first place. Luckily for him, they never found out.

In late January, 1979, two FBI men parked in the motel's car lot. They made their way to room 64 and knocked. Some shuffling sounds came from inside and then a woozy voice, "Who is it?" Dave had just woken up from an afternoon doze.

"FBI, we need to speak to you," said the bigger of the two men.

"What about?" asked Dave.

"Open the damn door, Riley. We got a big problem. We need you down at the station, fast."

There was a moment of silence and then the door eased open. Dave was in a vest and jogging pants. "Hey, look I thought we had an understanding, officers," he said to the two men standing outside.

"We did, but you haven't been all that useful to us lately and we've been hearing things about you and gunrunning scams," said the bigger of the two FBI officers.

Dave scratched his head, peeped further out of the doorway and said, "Come in. I got something you might want to know."

The men walked into the room and sniffed at the stale air, looking around at the mess on the floor.

"What a shit hole," said the shorter, blond guy, screwing his nose up.

"Yeah, well I haven't had time to spring clean yet," sneered Riley. "If I'd known you were coming..."

"Spill, Riley," interrupted the other officer. "We haven't come here to admire the décor."

"OK, now I didn't tell you this... Deal?" Riley sat on the edge of the bed.

"Goes without saying," said the blond guy.

"OK, one of my cars is being driven by a guy called Freddie Short, an annoying little fucker who hangs around here all the time. He's heading North on I-95 in Georgia, carrying a trunk load of guns and cigarettes to New York. If you hurry you'll catch him," Dave smiled and went over to the door and opened it. "Have a nice day, officers."

The Feds intercepted Short's car in North Carolina. Short resisted and in the ensuing shootout, took several bullets to the head, killing him instantly. It was over in a minute. He was no match for the firepower of ten FBI agents. Dave had done his part and handed the police yet another troublesome con. Dave didn't give it a second thought. He was glad to be rid of Freddie Short.

A MONTH LATER, ENSURING that Jo was out on an errand, Dave crept into her office and pried open the locks on the drawers in her desk. He shuffled through piles of papers, until he found what he was looking for.

"Nice." he thought.

JoAnne's property and bank account records showed that she owned some real estate and land in New Jersey. Dave locked her desk drawers and went back to his room. When Jo returned from her errands, Dave was waiting for her outside her office with coffee in hand.

"Hi, Jo. How are you today?" he said, smiling.

"I'm busy, David." Jo went to walk off, but Dave put a hand on her arm.

"It won't take long. Come sit down have some coffee with me."

By the following week, her big South River family house on Whitehead Street where she once lived and worked as a beautician, was now up for a quick sale, after persuasion from Dave.

"Remember why you're doing this, Jo. This is for the fight. The government will be thanking you soon and you'll get it all back, and then some." he assured.

Her old New Jersey home was sold, through Dave's lawyer Nathan Lomax, on the 5th of March, 1979, for $22,800. Some land she owned on the Turnpike, a mile from the house, was sold by Lomax for $10,000 the following day. Another piece of land bought years earlier as an investment by JoAnne, with a car repair shop on it, was also sold and went for around $10,000. That was it. All her worldly goods and real estate she had worked for, to keep her and her family secure after her retirement, gone. Riley and Lomax had liquidated all of it—nearly. There were still a couple more fine details they had to nail down.

The duo hit their favorite Miami bar that night, to celebrate their windfall, where they knew the management and staff. Dave chatted with the manager Paolo for a while and then turned to Lomax, who was laughing at the fact that Jo still believed that Riley was a federal agent and that she was helping the cause. Lomax, like Dave, was enjoying the subterfuge and drama.

"James Bond eat your heart out, huh Dave?" Lomax smirked, swilling expensive scotch around in his mouth, looking like an extra from Saturday Night Fever in his polyester shirt and flared pants. "Seems that this Jo broad will believe anything we tell her. I always wanted to be a secret agent!"

But Dave didn't want to be lumped into the same bracket as rat-faced Lomax, or any other one of his countless cronies. He saw himself as a cut above all the low-rent street hustlers and riffraff he considered were under his gainful employment.

"I work for the Feds, I told you, you stupid fucking shit! I'm their top man and don't forget that. I do what I want, when I want." he reminded Lomax.

"Hey, relax. We're fucking rich, man!" Lomax reminded Dave.

"No. Not yet, we're not."

Dave was never happy. The following day he cashed in two of the three life insurance policies JoAnne held from Polish National Alliance Insurance Company of Chicago, each worth a few thousand dollars. For some reason, only known to Dave, he didn't sell the third policy and left it for JoAnne.

Dave had one more property to lay his hands on though. On March 18, 1979, Riley brought JoAnne take-out over from Capra's. He then proceeded to convinced JoAnne to sell her beloved Biscayne Plaza Motel. While her memory of that day is hazy, she does remember Dave handing her the pen to sign the paperwork and hurrying her along. The motel went for a quick $120,000. She never fully understood why she signed the paperwork, but does remember the presence of Riley and Lomax, breathing down her neck as she sat at her desk.

"Just put your signature there, on that line." He stabbed his index finger on the white sheet of paper.

It was sold through Nathan Lomax's business named, "We Recommend," also based from his office on Bird Road in Miami.

JoAnne never saw a penny.

There was nothing that Nathan Lomax wouldn't do for a fast buck. He didn't care about the law or who he double crossed. Next target on the list was Riley. With the $120,000 from the sale of the motel in his hands, he decided there was no way that he was going to hand the money over to anyone, particularly Riley, who in his mind couldn't possibly need it more than he.

One night, Dave's bodyguard Lance, heard some interesting gossip while out drinking at one of the underground drinking dens in Miami where the Mob and criminals rubbed shoulders. That night, when he turned up at the motel to guard Dave's room while he slept, Lance knocked at the door of room 64. He was always obediently on time, so Dave answered straight away.

"Hi boss," said Lance. "I got some information for you."

"Oh yeah?" said Dave. He motioned for Lance to step into the room.

"Lomax has been bragging around town that he ripped you off."

"What d'you mean?" Dave asked.

"He says he rigged the paperwork for the sale of the motel so you don't get a penny."

Dave's eyes went into slits, "He said what?!"

"He's been telling everyone that'll listen, that he hit the jackpot and that you're a dumb sucker."

"Thanks, Lance. I owe you one." Riley grabbed his coat and marched out the door.

Nathan Lomax was found the same night with a single bullet to the head. At the time, he was staying at one of the top hotels in the Miami Beach on Fountainbleau Drive. The hotel was of such power back then, it was able to keep certain stories out of the press. The Miami Beach Police were known to be bought and sold throughout the years, and dating as far back to the 1920s, were usually able to keep the Mob and wealthy beach territories separated.

The Chicago and New York mobsters had an unwritten rule. There should be no killings on Miami Beach. It was to be a place of neutral territory. Some things had to remain sacred. Though, when it came to Lomax, no one cared where his blood was spilt, beach or no precious beach.

Dave never uncovered the missing cash from the sale of the motel, however that wasn't the point. It riled him that he had missed out on thousands of dollars, but something offended him much more. It was the principle. He didn't like it when his friends double crossed him. In his mind, it just wasn't morally right. Lomax deserved that bullet, Dave conceded.

No one was arrested over Nathan Lomax's shooting and the incident was reported in the papers as suicide.

SEVENTEEN

D AYS PRIOR TO THE sale of the Biscayne Plaza Motel in March 1979, Riley stole and sold Jo's Plymouth, so she was homeless and without any means of transport. A friend and former employee at the motel let her stay in the living room of her small apartment nearby and Jo found a job as a hair stylist.

One evening, at about eight o'clock, there was a loud knock at the door. JoAnne was in the place alone and went to see who it was.

The shock hit her at once. "What're you doing here?"

An unshaven Dave leaned on the wall outside. "Hey there, Jo. I thought I'd look you up. Pleased to see me?"

"You can't stay here!" she told him and went to slam the door in his face. Dave shoved it back open with his boot.

"Look, I haven't come to cause any trouble. I've come to help you," he said.

"I'm fine, really," Jo replied.

"But you can't stay here indefinitely," said Riley. "I've got family who'll help us. C'mon I feel real bad about what's happened. Once the government pays you up, you can get your own place again. 'Til then I'm gonna sort you out."

Dave took JoAnne to his cousin Andrew's house, south of Miami. Andrew Riley was the son of the brother of Dave's father and around ten years older than his cousin. Andrew made it known that he was annoyed.

"Get your life together, David. You're almost 40 now. You can't carry on like this forever."

Dave sat on Andrew's sofa, chewing on a sandwich he'd just been handed. Jo overheard the converation from the other room.

"Yeah, I know," Dave replied. "You don't need to get on my back. I didn't come here for a lecture."

"Sort your damn life out then!"

He and Jo were only there for two or three days before Dave took off with his bodyguards. Andrew and his wife drove Jo to Miami, where another female motel operator, based a stone's throw from the sold Biscayne Plaza Motel, took her in.

A few days passed and Dave showed up on the doorstep again. JoAnne never figured out how he was always able to find her whereabouts, but Riley with a wide circle of contacts easily had Jo followed or found, whatever her address. There was nothing that Dave hadn't made it his business to find out about JoAnne and her background.

"Look, all our problems will be over when we get to Emily's house in Dallas. She'll look out for us," Dave said.

"How'd you know about Emily?" asked Jo.

"You told me about her loads of times."

Emily Thurston was a longtime family friend of Jo's from New Jersey who, with her husband Mike, had settled in the center of Dallas. So, with Dave's two huge body guards, the four made it to

Dallas in early April 1979, in a second hand car bought out of Jo's final pay check from the beauty shop.

When they parked outside the Thurstons' four bedroom house, Dave got out of the car and walked to the door. He turned to Lance and his other bodyguard and warned, "You two, be polite. These are nice people."

"OK boss," said a smirking Lance.

A woman in her early 50s opened the door. "Who're you?" she asked immediately, seeing Dave's sidekicks. She then faced JoAnne. "What's going on? Mike, can you come here?! Mike!" she shouted down the hallway to her husband.

Jo was about to explain the situation to her friend when Dave jumped in.

"Hi, I'm Dave, the friend JoAnne told you about on the phone." He smiled and held out his hand for Emily's husband Mike to shake. Mike stood there, glaring at Dave and then warily eyeing Lance.

"We haven't got room for all of you," barked Emily, nodding towards the two big men behind Dave.

"OK, you two make yourselves scarce. I'll call you later," Riley said to Lance and his other bodyguard.

JoAnne was put in a spare bedroom and Dave was on the sofa in the living room. Within a week Dave had managed to befriend Mike Thurston.

"You wanna make some money? Then you stick with me," said Riley.

Emily and Jo were out grocery shopping.

"What d'you want me to do?" asked Mike, a straight up guy and not suspecting for one minute that Riley was talking about anything illegal.

"It's just the same as being a mailman. All you gotta do is take stuff to different addresses for me."

"That sounds really easy," said Mike.

Everyday Dave sent Mike out on errands that involved passing packages of drugs and other illicit goods to the local low life's in the area, with whom Dave had made it his business to hook up within days of getting to Dallas. Emily, the feisty half of the couple, wasn't happy.

"I don't trust Riley," she told her husband, "He wants to cook, but I told him that no one but me does anything in that kitchen."

In her view, she was happy to provide Jo with a roof over her head. After all, they went back years and Emily had even babysat Jo's kids when she was at work years before. But, she had heard enough about Riley to be wary. She was suspicious that he would poison her and Mike, who was now disappearing for days at a time.

When she asked Dave where her husband was he said, "He's on a secret federal mission for me. Don't worry, it's all for a good cause."

Emily never knew whether to believe him or not. On one hand, she wanted her husband to do his bit for the country, but on the other hand she had suspicions about her new house guest.

"What is it you do again?" She asked Dave one evening while she prepared dinner. Dave sat at the table watching her peel potatoes.

"Important federal work. We're near to getting rid of the commie's altogether. All we need is an injection of cash and our job's nearly done," he said. It wasn't the first time he had dropped hints for money.

"I'm not rich…" Emily said.

"We'll be grateful for whatever you can manage. The government will reimburse you anyhow," Dave replied quickly.

"You're sure I'll get it all back?"

"And then some!" Riley gave her one of his winning smiles and put his hand on his chest. "You got my word on that."

Emily looked at him seriously. "Your word? You promise?"

"I Promise—on my mother's life."

Emily handed over several thousand dollars. However, within weeks she wised up to the fact that her initial gut reaction to Riley was correct. She threw Dave and JoAnne out without as much as a "bye" to her once good friend.

Dave disappeared from sight and headed back to Miami. Jo had little money in her purse, so she made her way to her younger brother Kobe's home in Tampa, where he had been attempting to reunite with his once estranged wife, Cindy and their daughter, Amanda. The reunion hadn't worked out as Kobe had hoped and he was now living in a room nearby.

Meantime, Emily Thurston got on the phone to JoAnne's sister, Halena Marek, demanding to know when she would be reimbursed for the money she had given Dave for his federal work. The two women exchanged extremely strong words. Halena then pointing out that it wasn't her fault and that she too had been fleeced of $20,000 herself by Dave and her dry goods business in New Jersey was in dire trouble. In fact, it was on the verge of closing down as Halena didn't have the funds to buy new stock.

PENNILESS, JOANNE WAS SENT on housekeeping and aiding the infirmed assignments by an employment agency. She then settled in as a worker at the John Knox Retirement Center in Tampa, working long hours so she could amass enough cash to rent a place of her own. She didn't want to be a burden on her family any longer. JoAnne had just set herself up in a tiny apartment in a converted garage on the grounds of a local woman's house, Ellen Ward, on Ellicott Street in Tampa.

One morning she was heading out to work when she felt a presence behind her. She spun around.

"How did you find me?" she gasped.

Dave shrugged. "I've got no place to go."

"I can't help you!" JoAnne looked at her watch. She didn't want to be late for her shift.

Dave moved forward. "Please."

It was the first of many nights that he slept on a mattress on the floor of JoAnne's new two-room converted garage.

IN JUNE OF 1979, JoAnne's niece, 18-year-old Amanda, a stunning dark-haired girl, and "A" student, graduated from Tampa Bay High School, with both her parents, Cindy and Kobe, in the crowd, cheering her on.

The summer was here and a teenage Amanda was itching for adventure with her studies over. No more than 10 days after her graduation, in breezed Dave. He was soon enjoying alternate afternoons of sex in the same local motel room with both mother and daughter, unbeknownst to them. But Amanda found out what was going on and flew out of the house, with her aunt JoAnne running after her.

"Surely, you've got it wrong, Amanda," said Jo as her niece

sprinted towards the motel. "Dave wouldn't be sleeping with you both. She is your mom."

Amanda laughed dryly. "Oh yeah, like that matters. She doesn't care. She's jealous because I'm younger and prettier than her!" She said as she raced towards a red brick run-down motel no more than two blocks from her family home.

Amanda and Cindy didn't know it then, but Dave had also been spending random nights at the larger Beaumont Motel down the road, where he had met his new girlfriend, Bonnie Dell, who was staying in a room with her two small children.

Riley was in his element. His three women residing practically in the same street, right under each other's noses, and two of them were related, even better.

Amanda barged into the lobby of the motel and up to the bellboy on reception, demanding Dave's room number. Furious when she found out that her mother was in the same room she herself had been staying in with Dave. She flew down the hallway, and banged loudly at the door.

"Mom! Open this door!" she yelled. Cindy and Dave were shocked by the sound of Amanda's voice. Dave threw on his clothes and went to the door, opening it slightly, not bargaining on the young girl's strength. The door sprang wide open and Amanda stormed into the room, with JoAnne behind her.

"Amanda! What're you doing here?" asked a naked Cindy, hurriedly reaching for her lace panties and pulling them on.

"More like, what are you doing here, mother?" replied Amanda with a disapproving sneer.

Dave was sitting on the edge of the bed, trying to suppress a smile while he pulled on his cowboy boots.

"I can't believe you've been sleeping with my boyfriend!" yelled Amanda.

JoAnne tried to hold her niece back, telling her to calm down, but Amanda elbowed her away.

"Boyfriend?" Cindy's face drained of color and she turned to glare at Dave, who shrugged. "You are joking? You've been sleeping together?" Now almost fully dressed, she then faced Amanda.

"She just told me," said JoAnne. "Cindy, calm down!"

"Uh-huh, that's right. You were always jealous!" Amanda shouted at her mother.

As quick as a flash, Cindy felt hot rage fill her body. She grabbed her gold sandals and then her daughter by the arm, pulling her towards the door. She glared at Dave. "You keep away from my daughter, creep!" she warned, waving her high heels in the air, and then she told Amanda,"You're coming home with me, girl!"

"Get off me, Mom!" and after a struggle, ran to Dave and sat beside him on the bed. Dave then stood up between Cindy and Amanda. Cindy screamed at Dave to move away and then reached around Dave and dragged her daughter into the hallway.

"Let go. I'll be back home in a few days, mom. Stop fussing!" Amanda yelled and pulled away from Cindy, again.

"Please don't go in that room with him! Amanda!" cried a still barefoot Cindy as the two women struggled. JoAnne was also pulling at her niece's t-shirt, trying to move her down the hall.

"Listen to your mother!" said JoAnne.

Riley then grabbed Amanda around the waist, heaving her towards the door of the room, while Cindy grappled roughly at the back of his shirt, trying to maneuver around him so she could act as a barrier between him and her daughter.

Dave then grabbed a hold of Cindy's fists, which were about to land on the side of his head with an almighty thud.

"Fuck off! Home, Cindy. You silly bitch!" Dave pushed her away and threw Amanda into his room, slamming the door shut behind her.

"Get away from my daughter, you disgusting pervert!" Cindy screamed and swiped at Dave with her shoes, but he ducked in time. "Amanda! I'm begging you! Please! Come out of there!"

"Go away, mom!" shouted Amanda through the door. "Leave us alone!"

Dave smiled at Cindy, now wailing in the arms of a furious JoAnne, mascara tracks trailing down her cheeks.

"Open the door, Dave. The girl's just 18," Jo called.

Opening the door a crack and slipping into the room Dave answered, "We're going on a short trip to Colorado. We'll be back in a week. I'll send you both a postcard if you like." With that, he laughed and shut the door.

Amanda was more headstrong than ever and had ignored her mother's orders not to go anywhere near Dave, and now she had just disappeared into a seedy motel with him and was about to go away with him. Riley took Amanda on a trip to Colorado Springs for a week.

While she was gone, Kobe and Cindy were frantic with worry. Kobe also found out from neighbors about his estranged wife's relationship with Riley and was absolutely livid.

Amanda thought Dave was exciting, dangerous, different from the silly boys in her hometown. Dave had seen the world and when planning the trip to Colorado Springs, he promised her a stop in

Miami, talking excitedly of music executives, recording studios
and his past as a singer and songwriter. Dave regaled Amanda with
stories of being in with the Mafia and how he was close buddies
with Frank Sinatra, having hung out and dined with him at Capra's
when he lived at the motel.

"Oh yeah, me and Frank were like that," Dave said, crossing
his two middle fingers together in front of his face. "He'd sit at his
favorite table and order scotch on the rocks and a plate of spaghetti
and meatballs. Then we'd sit and chew the fat till the early hours."
Amanda lapped it all up.

Dave told her that he was going to take her to Cheyenne
Mountain NORAD, North American Aerospace Defense
Command, in Colorado Springs where the U.S. and Canada monitor
the world's missile and satellite activities and can order a retaliatory
nuclear attack with the famous 'red phone' on the President's
desk. The 24/7 operation, deep inside a granite mountain does
not permit visitors near the highly secret and complex equipment
capable of firing nuclear warheads from North Dakota and many
other far away nuclear posts. Dave made it clear to Amanda that
he was going there to carry out some important work for the
government.

When they arrived, Dave left Amanda in the car with his two
bodyguards. She was overawed by the sight of the imposing dark
mountainside, designed to sustain a nuclear bomb if dropped there,
Whether Dave was doing business at the site or simply perpetuating
a charade, is uncertain, though it is questionable that Dave had top
security clearance to enter the place.

Amanda imagined she had met a sophisticated, older man who
could show her the high life. But there was only one thing that

Dave wanted from Amanda. He liked his women very young and naive. As he drew closer to middle-age, the more youthful his girlfriends got, and the more deviant his sexual tastes became.

Nearly a week after Dave and Amanda left Tampa, the couple booked into a motel in Colorado. At 2AM, when sounds of a young girl screaming and loud crashes of breaking furniture began radiating through the wall in addition to the voice of a man shouting, "Shut the fuck up, whore!," the couple in the room next door called the police.

When the Colorado Springs Police broke into the room, they found Amanda naked on the bed, half-comatose, covered in cuts and bruises, her hands tied in front of her and blood covering the white sheets. Clumps of her long hair had been yanked out, leaving bald patches on her scalp. There was a pile of cocaine and marijuana on the bedside table and hypodermic needles strewn on the floor. Dave was nowhere to be seen. He had absconded into the night seconds before the cops turned up and bashed in the door.

Amanda was lucky to be alive. If the police had gotten there any later, she wouldn't have been so fortunate, said the doctor at the local hospital. Thanks to the couple in the next room, Amanda survived. When Amanda was released from the hospital her Aunt Halena paid for her plane ticket back home.

Kidnapping charges were dropped against Dave. Amanda had just passed her 18th birthday by a few weeks and since she didn't press assault charges, Dave escaped prosecution.

EIGHTEEN

I N RETURN FOR HIS continued freedom following the *Black Friday* case, part of the deal was that Riley was obliged to report to his parole officer every fortnight at a set time in Miami, but Dave had it in his head that he had done so many favors for the police, FBI and ATF, by giving them the names of countless criminals, that he was untouchable. He came to the conclusion that the parole agreement didn't stand, not that he was officially told this. So, it was something of a shock to Dave, when on January 20, 1980 he was arrested on a parole violator's warrant.

After being questioned by the police about breaking parole, Dave ended up at the Marshall's Federal Court lockup in Miami, being interviewed by William P. Gersen III, an attorney hired by Halena Marek and her brother Kobe. They intended to sue Riley and the estate of Nathan Lomax, and wanted to know what had happened to Halena's $20,000 loan and to all of JoAnne's cash and the money from the sales of her properties. They both agreed Dave was drugging their sister, so it was up to them to act on her behalf.

Gersen had been working on a separate case to sue the Lomax

estate for four-hundred-thousand dollars, so was well aware of Riley's doings. A former prosecutor, Gersen, was in his late fifties and after spending years in a courtroom, he had had his fill of what he termed losers. When Dave was brought into the court meeting room by two policemen, he had Riley summed up on sight, as a jumped up, opportunistic scumbag with an inflated sense of his own self-importance. Gersen wasn't about to let Dave off lightly. He wanted the truth before this guy was to walk out.

Dave was sitting, facing Gersen, elbows resting on his knees as he looked the other man in the eye and shrugged, "Yeah, me and my lawyer, Nathan Lomax, we sold Jo's properties."

"So, where did all the money go?" asked Gersen.

Dave smiled. "It's gone, I guess."

"What do you mean, you guess? Where has it gone?"

Another shrug came from Riley and he sat up straight. "It got spent on stuff."

"Mrs. Halena Marek says JoAnne never saw a dime from the motel sale or any of the other transactions you arranged for the New Jersey properties. Can you explain what exactly happened to all this money, please, Mr. Riley?"

Dave crossed his legs and tipped his head to one side. Gersen could hardly stomach his blasé demeanor.

"OK, I guess you've got me there. It's all gone, like I said. Gersen, did you say your name was?"

The attorney nodded, stifling the urge to wipe the smirk off of the puny runt's face with his bare hand.

Dave took out his cigarettes and offered one to Gersen, who shook his head. Dave flicked a Marlboro into the air and caught it between his teeth. "Cool name, but I always preferred Bogart myself. *African Queen*, now that's a classic movie."

Gersen's broad forehead creased in frustration. "We're not here to discuss movie stars."

Dave shrugged. "OK."

"Why did you rip off Mrs. Novak?" Gersen barked.

"Because it was easy," said Dave. "If she wanted to give me money, who was I to stop her?"

Gersen snorted. "You're a piece of work."

"Thanks," replied Dave with a smirk.

On April 11, 1980, William P. Gersen III wrote an official letter to the Honorable Janet Reno, State Attorney for Dade County at the Metropolitan Justice Building NW 12th Street, Miami. It stated that David Riley had an extensive FBI record, including kidnapping and air piracy.

In the last few paragraphs Gersen explained, "During my conversation, Mr. Riley admitted Lomax swindled, along with his help, Mrs. Novak out of real estate properties and gave her no money in return. Riley said he and Lomax planned to use the back of the Biscayne Plaza Motel to store bales of marijuana and use the front for prostitution purposes."

Soon after Dave's meeting with Gersen, Halena and Kobe received a letter from JoAnne, ordering them to halt their legal action against David Riley, saying they could easily jeopardize the important and sensitive government work in which she and Dave were involved. Reluctantly, JoAnne's brother and sister followed the desist order and William P. Gersen was asked to drop the case.

Dave told Jo, "We can't go on with our government work with this interference from Halena and Kobe."

JoAnne was not interested in Riley romantically or physically, nor did she see herself as a mother figure towards him. She was her own woman. Subconsciously, though, she was searching for more in life. She wanted to be important, to do something significant. In her mind, Dave's government work gave her the opportunity to make a difference in a momentous way. She figured it wasn't every day that a woman like her got the chance to make a mark.

Around the time of the sale of the Biscayne Plaza Motel, JoAnne's son, Ben had flown to visit her from his home in Stamford, Connecticut. Like his Aunt Halena and Uncle Kobe, Ben was certain Dave was drugging his mother on a regular basis.

"Mom, you've not been acting like your normal self for the last year. Please, let me take you to a doctor," said Ben.

Jo was in her office, sitting at her desk, clutching the prayer book that she had been carryng with her practically everywhere. She looked thin and drawn and Ben could see that the life had drained from her. It was a frightening sight. He dropped to his knees and placed his hands in the begging position, looking up at his mother.

"Mom, please, before it's too late." But Jo wasn't listening.

Dave deduced from the very beginning that he had stumbled upon a never-ending well of ready made resources. He came up with the plan that after he got all of JoAnne's assests, he would then go through all of her friends and family, one by one. Next on his hit list was JoAnne's son, Ben. Having heard from Jo that Ben was having relationship problems with his wife, Bernice Miller, Riley suggested that he should pay Ben a visit in Connecticut.

Bitter court battles over Ben's property and money had pushed Ben's once happy marriage with the fiery fashion buyer, Bernice, into an area of no return.

"It breaks my heart to think of a smart young guy like Ben going through so much alone," said Dave to Jo. "I'm going to use my important contacts to get him out of this legal mess."

A classically good-looking guy with the family work ethic, Ben was a skilled computer technician for General Electric, commuting each day to the office in New York City. He had met Bernice at a mutual friend's barbecue five years before and was initially knocked out by her beauty. Grown men nearly broke their necks craning for a better look at the statuesque auburn-haired Bernice, and Ben was no different. He was just a regular guy, who liked baseball and kept fit by running on weekends. However, his wife proved too demanding. She had such expensive tastes in clothes and restaurants that Ben found it hard to keep her happy for long. Her greed for a flashy lifestyle ended their relationship and now she was out for blood. Being his wife, and the mother of his two young daughters, she was legally entitled to half of everything he owned. Ben had hired leading New Hampshire-based lawyer, Leo Michaels, to fight her in court.

Ben never dealt with anyone like Dave Riley before and felt conflicted, but was willing to consider that Dave was well connected and be able to lever him out of his legal mire. Ben, an organized man, kept a log of all of phone calls and movements and everything else that was happening in his own house.

On January 12, 1981, Ben wrote in his log that he received a collect phone call from his mother, JoAnne.

"Can I borrow $200, Ben?" she said, sounding rattled. Ben could hear a male voice in the background.

"I'm broke, Mom. The court case against Bernice is costing me thousands," answered Ben.

"Don't worry. I know someone who can help resolve all your legal problems," she said.

"Really. Who?"

And in from the wings stepped Dave, leaning in behind Jo as she spoke on the telephone in her apartment, "The conditions are that Ben follows all orders, do as he is told, and cover all expenses," he whispered into her ear.

JoAnne relayed the conditions to Ben, who then asked, "Is this all legal and honest?"

"Yes, of course," said Jo.

"What are the expenses?"

Riley snatched the phone off JoAnne.

"The money's needed to get any initial moves against Bernice underway. And I'll need an additional $1000, but that'll be reimbursed."

"I don't know let me think about it," said Ben.

"I'll call you tomorrow," said Dave.

In the next collect call, Riley requested $600 to be wired to him and the money was used for a car rental for two of Riley's men, Carlos Arnaldo Torres and Gerald Ramirez. David Montez, Riley traveling under his alias traveled by plane to Connecticut.

A few days later, Ben was watching a football game on TV when there was a heavy knock on the front door. He opened the door and there stood Dave Riley and two other guys. Gerald Ramirez was a hulk of a man with a grizzled leathery face that would have scared the living daylights out of anyone. Arnaldo Torres wasn't much prettier.

Ben was immediately on guard, but offered the the trio beef sandwiches he had made for them. They all grabbed a place on the sofa.

Dave was bright and breezy, "Ben buddy, you stick with me and soon all your troubles will be behind you."

"I hope so."

"Trust me." Riley took another chunk out of his sandwich and grinned. "Nice house you got here." He craned his neck, scoping out the place.

"Look guys. I don't have enough room here for the three of you. I'm sorry." Ben really didn't like the look of Ramirez, who took up most of the leather sofa placed against the opposite wall of his living room.

The visitors agreed to stay in the nearby Ramada Inn for a few nights and on his way out Dave had some whispered information for Ben, "We've got Bernice under surveillance, but there's one more thing we need."

"What?" Ben asked, opening the front door.

"More equipment. But it costs," replied Dave.

"How much?"

"A thousand dollars, but then we can keep an eye on the scheming witch for you," said Dave. "All we gotta do is get it all down on tape and she'll looks like a dumb fucking slut in court."

"OK," Ben ushered the three men out of his house.

On January 23, 1981, Ben, as Dave requested, wired the money to a Jesse Ponders c/o United States Auto Radiators on Bird Road Miami in order to buy equipment to be placed in Bernice's house, to monitor all her phone calls.

"I don't feel comfortable about this." Ben said during Riley's next unannounced visit to his home.

"We have to up our game, Ben." Riley told him. "Bernice is having your phones tapped. They're listening to all your calls.

Pretty heavy, huh?"

"Yeah." replied Ben, now paranoid.

"Relax, I'm here for you, bud." Dave squeezed Ben's shoulder and off he and his men went.

The following afternoon Ben met Riley and his two cronies at the Ramada Inn, to wait for the phone tapping equipment to be delivered. Only, nothing materialized, until the next day when a young guy named Ponders showed up at Ben's place with a bald Hispanic man named Curley, who slapped a large bag on the glass top of his kitchen table. Dave rummaged through the bag, pulling out a Magnum revolver, an MI6 automatic rifle and a single-barreled shotgun.

"Nice stuff," he said, caressing the goods and smiling at Ponders, a black guy with cornrows.

Ponders cackled. "You got that right, man."

"But where's the equipment I paid you for?" cried Ben, his eyes widening at the sight of the heavy weaponry. "What are the guns for?"

Ponders, Curley, Torres and Ramirez looked at one another and laughed.

"Is this kid for fucking real?" asked Ponders.

"Look guys" Ben went to leave the room, but Dave stopped him.

"We put the phone tapping stuff someplace else, for safe-keeping," He motioned to the revolvers. "Oh these, they're nothing. They're for another job. Federal security. These guys are all special agents."

Ben didn't look convinced. Ramirez and Torres in particular had an air about them that made you assume they had just finished a twenty year stretch in a high security jail.

"The court case against you is about to be dropped and Bernice won't be showing her face in court now," announced Dave.

Ben frowned. "How come you only just remembered to tell me this?"

"I had a lot on my mind. I'm a busy man," replied Dave.

Coincidentally, a court hearing was cancelled days later and Dave crowed to Ben that it was all down to his influence. That he had arranged it so that they would be given more time to set up additional plans.

The following morning Dave called Ben asking him for an additional $2000, also announcing that Bernice was in collusion with Ben's lawyer, Leo Michaels, and that something untoward was going on between them.

"I'll call you when I find out more," whispered Dave on the phone in his best private investigator's voice. "I can't talk now. People are listening in, but I'm onto something big, real juicy."

All this cloak and dagger stuff was adding to Ben's agitated state and after speaking to JoAnne about the money she and Dave were asking for, he was assured again that Riley would indeed pay him back. Calmed by his mother's words, Ben handed over $2000 in cash to Riley.

That night Dave and his men were at Ben's door demanding to be let in. Dave pushed his way past Ben, into the hall.

"You're under armed guard now, bud. We gotta be careful. The whole house is being bugged!" Dave opened his sports jacket and flashed Ben his pistol. He then grabbed Ben by the shoulders and dragged him upstairs. "This is dangerous stuff. You shut yourself in your room and read a book or something. I'll let you know when you can come out."

"But." Ben was terrified.

"I haven't fucking got time for this! You want to keep safe you stay in your room!" Dave pushed Ben into his bedroom, slammed the door and ordered one of his men to act as a guard outside while Dave went about his business.

Days later, Riley demanded that Ben hand over another $2000, promising that Bernice would be gone soon.

"Good, but I haven't got any more money. This is it," said Ben, fearful for his diminishing bank balance.

The following night Ben was sitting, watching TV when there was a deafening bang at the door. When he opened it Dave, Ponders, Ramirez, Torres and Curley were standing there, bags in hands, and they pushed past him, pulling out chairs, sitting around the kitchen table like it was a local diner.

"We're moving in," announced Riley.

"What?!" Ben was incredulous.

"We gotta step up the campaign. Your lawyer isn't playing ball. They got people everywhere," said Dave. "Coffee guys?"

Dave's buddies put in drinks requests, which Ben reluctantly went about making.

"You're one hell of a good dude," said Dave, smacking Ben on the back.

Dave held his coffee cup in the air, proposing a toast. "To Ben!"

"Look, this is my home," said Ben, pleading as tears shone in his eyes. "You have to get out."

Riley was sick to death of Ben's moaning. He looked at him with a serious expression and leaned in close.

"We're here to help you. You wouldn't want to seem ungrateful, now would you?" Dave opened his jacket so that a flash of his pistol showed.

"No."

"Good." Dave pushed Ben roughly out of the way and carried on speaking while he put two slices of bread in the toaster. "Leo Michaels is laughing at you. We gotta keep up the pressure."

The next day Ben couldn't track down his lawyer in New Hampshire to discuss a rescheduled court date, so Ben asked Dave what was going on.

"Hey, I didn't want to tell you this, but I found out something…" Riley was leaning against the living room door frame, wearing a weary expression. "Bernice is in Vermont, in some swanky motel, fucking your lawyer's brains out. You can't trust anyone Ben, even your own lawyer, man! How low is that? If he was banging my girl I'd beat his brains out. I'm the only one that can protect you now, bud."

"I can't believe this is happening," sighed Ben.

"I got something else you should know," said Dave.

"Huh?" mumbled Ben.

"Your friend… You watch your back."

"Ray?" Raymond Winston was a close pal of Ben's, who was staying in the spare room a few nights a week, until he found a new apartment.

"He's spying on you. He's an informant for Bernice and Leo Michaels," replied Dave.

"I don't believe you. Ray wouldn't do that."

"I told you! You gotta trust me!" Riley's face was contorted with rage.

Ben stood and edged toward the door. "Look, Dave all this is getting out of hand. I want you to go."

"If you don't do exactly as I say, then this court case will never end and you'll be bankrupt."

Ben was in a state. "What the hell is going on? There're strange people in my home night and day. My mother is acting weird. I don't see any results. Bernice is still on my back. I just want to see my kids."

"Patience." snapped Dave. "Trust me. I keep fucking tellin' you!" He smashed his hand into the living room door, leaving a dent in the wooden panel.

Out of sheer desperation, Ben ran out of his house and drove like crazy to Stamford Police station to ask them to get Riley out. Police Chief Robert Mason immediately knew Ben's address and stated that the cops had been watching the place 24/7.

"What for?" asked Ben.

"We know you're involved in dealing drugs." he said. "We think you're the head guy."

"What? Me? You're kidding!"

"You're the one running the operation," said Mason, a broad-shouldered guy with a neatly clipped moustache.

Ben felt sick to his stomach. Now it dawned on him why Dave had been locking him in his room each night.

"Drugs? At my house?"

Mason nodded and gave Ben a know-it-all smile. "Heroin… cocaine…thousands of dollars worth of the stuff's being sold outta your place every week. And we know that you're up to your neck in it, so don't play innocent with me Ben."

Ben felt the ground move beneath him. He put his hand on the wall and took a few deep breaths. Then he looked at Mason.

"I don't know anything about any of this. I'm no drug dealer. It's all down to David Riley. You've got to help me get him out!"

Mason sighed. "OK, Mr. Novak, whatever you say." He'd heard it all before and he couldn't be bothered to argue. He began to read Ben his Miranda Rights, "I am advising you, anything you say may be used against you in a court of law..."

"Why won't you listen to me?" cut in Ben. "I need help! I'm not a drug dealer. This has nothing to do with me!"

Realizing that Mason wasn't listening to a word he said, Ben felt waves of panic engulf him and he bolted for the door of the station. The police chief didn't move a muscle. Ben hadn't said that he understood the accusations leveled against him while he had been read his rights. Ben hadn't admitted any guilt.

Mason wasn't buying Ben's act. He was damn sure that if Ben was inviting renowned dealers into his home, then he must be involved in the operation. Ben had let Riley into his home. Mason walked to the front window of the station and watched a defeated Ben walk to his car. He decided that he would let him go for the time being.

On February 14, 1981, Riley and Ben's mother demanded $1,450.00 cash be wired to Gold Shield Detective Agency in Hollywood, Florida.

"I'm not handing over another cent," Ben said.

Jo then phoned and asked Ben to sign a letter notarizing Dave to act on his behalf, requesting for him to resolve all legal matters between him and Bernice. Dave was panicking. He felt that he was losing grip and wanted something in writing. Fed up and exhausted, Ben eventually signed the letter. Although he could see that his mother was acting differently to how she had before, yet he still loved and trusted her.

In the March of 1981, Ben received three more requests for money while at work. Dave called Ben again at his office at General Electric in New York City and asked for another $175 for expenses.

"I'm busy. Just leave me alone!" Ben slammed the receiver down.

A highly affronted Dave then persuaded JoAnne to get with Ben's sister, Katherine, and his friends, underlining Dave's urgent need for funds which were required in order to help Ben with his problems.

And then Hertz called, looking for a car they had rented to Dave in Ben's name. Ben was shocked at this and told the company that he had no idea where the car was. When he confronted Dave about it, he pleaded ignorance.

"I want some peace!" yelled Ben to Dave on the phone after work. "Keep your crooks away from me and don't ask for any more money. I'll sort out my own problems with Bernice. Please leave me alone. Hertz and God know's who else keeps calling night and day. They want their fucking car back!"

"Hey, bud. Don't sweat it. I'll be back in Connecticut to speak to the car company within 48 hours," cajoled Dave. "Jeez, talk about hysterical."

Ben hung up, but the peace didn't last and the phone rang again and again, 24/7. Dave had put it in Jo's head that her son was acting paranoid. Hearing his mom's concerns for his mental welfare, Ben began to wonder if it wasn't true. His finances were a mess and he couldn't concentrate at work.

On March 29, 1981, Ben wrote in his log that he received a

final call from Dave, "Well it looks like my efforts for you and your mom have gone unappreciated." Riley's voice was ice cold. "JoAnne told me you were in trouble and all I've done is try to help. She warned me that you don't take advice well."

"What?" Ben slumped down on his sofa.

"She begged me to help you. She said you were on a one way route to nowhere," sneered Dave. "And all you've done is whine like a big fucking baby."

"You're kidding, right?" Ben couldn't take it.

"She said you're just like your dad. Weak."

"He's dead. Leave him out of this," said Ben.

"Well, I'm finished with both you and your stupid mother. Good luck with the case, Benny boy." With that, Riley slammed the receiver down.

On April 2, 1981, Ben reported the rental car stolen to Stamford Police and went to the FBI and spoke to Agent Laurence Barr about Dave. When he returned home, Jo called to say that a telegram was on its way, listing all the work that Dave had undertaken on his behalf. Jo then asked Ben for $150. He refused. He knew Riley was with his mother and was telling her what to say.

JoAnne's voice was now halting and shaky, "Unless you send the money Dave says I'll be thrown in jail."

"Sorry, Mom. Bye."

Ben slammed the receiver down.

Ben asked his friend Raymond Winston to answer all phone calls including those from his mother. It was over. Dave's Connecticut drug operation was rendered defunct and its headquarters was moved back to Tampa, where Dave ran his heroin business out of motels once more.

Within days, Ben was called into the main office by his boss and fired. The police had informed General Electric about the narcotics operation operating out of Ben's home. General Electric didn't want a dealer on their workforce. The company also set up an alert on their computer database, informing all other such big corporations of Ben's recent descent into crime. No one would touch him professionally. Ben's career was over.

"You're finished," his boss told him.

As for Dave's dirt on Bernice Miller, the only time she had been up close and personal with Leo Michaels was when she passed him in the hallway at a court hearing. Though to Ben, even though his case with Bernice bankrupted Ben, it paled in significance after everything he had been through with Dave. In the end, his greatest regret was that his relationship with his two daughters was compromised as they sided with their mother after the court case.

For a time, following the Riley incident, Ben harbored resentment towards his mother, but soon his anger turned to concern over her welfare. He didn't have her new Ellicott Street address in Tampa, so he tried tracking her down through the Biscayne Plaza Motel phone number and then by registered letter to her last known address in Miami, hopeful it would find her. Shamed, Jo was hiding and vowed that she would not speak to her family until she had earned enough money to pay them back.

Dave made plans of his own. He headed to his girlfriend's room at the Beaumont Motel in Tampa and proposed to Bonnie Dell. Instead of a diamond ring he handed her a wrap of heroin. She was overjoyed.

NINETEEN

ANY WOMAN IN HER right mind would have avoided
Dave, but his access to drugs were a big temptation for
female users. Bonnie Dell had been taking cocaine for years. She
was a 28-year-old single mother of two, a boy and a girl, aged five
and seven. Bonnie met Dave at the Beaumont Motel where she
was staying while her home in Clearwater, 35 miles from Tampa
on the Gulf Coast, was being refurbished after a flood. Shortly
after meeting Dave, her use of narcotics rocketed into severe
addiction. In the 80s and early 90s, drugs were expensive and hard
to come by, so dealers like Riley were magnets for needy women
like Bonnie. Heroin became her drug of choice and Dave was her
supply.

Once a striking girl with a neat figure and hopes of being a
teacher, Bonnie spent her days doped up to her eyeballs, often while
her mother cared for her children. Although still attractive, her
blonde hair went unstyled and her face hadn't seen makeup in some
time. An unhealthy lifestyle had left her body out of shape, though a
tired beauty still shone out from her hazel eyes.

Bonnie Dell was a lost soul. Dave didn't love her any more than the others with whom he slept. Bonnie was someone he could control and Dave liked the fact that she was reliant on him. She fed his ego. For reasons, known only to her, it wasn't just the drugs she was addicted to, she was crazy about Dave. His interaction with JoAnne puzzled her. Even though she stayed at JoAnne's apartment with Dave on many occasions, she viewed Jo with a certain amount of suspicion.

As 1981 turned into 1982, Jo was still waiting for her money to be reimbursed by the government. She was working 12-hour shifts at a retirement center and Riley continued to scrounge cash or free board out of her whenever he was able. He spent many a night sleeping on her sofa.

Amanda and Cindy weren't the only women with whom Dave had affairs and Bonnie had a good idea of what was going on during the times he left her for days. He had a willing supply of females everywhere he went and used them and threw them away when he was done, but drugs no doubt amplified Bonnie's constant state of paranoia.

It was unclear why he bothered to stick with Bonnie, but it was thought by some that they had a daughter, although no one met the girl and Dave kept this part of his personal life quiet. However, JoAnne once overheard Dave shouting on the phone, "You're my daughter and you'll do as you're told!"

State records in New York and Florida show a daughter of Riley's having lived in New York and nine marriages listed in Florida alone in the 70s through 90s between David Thomas Riley and assorted women. There are six registered dissolution of marriages in Florida under his name from 1978 through 1999.

Dave took full advantage of the state's quick legal breakup, allowing dissolution if both parties agree to give up their right to a trial after living apart for six months. Unlike Bonnie Dell, at least half a dozen women were glad to see the back of Riley. For nine years she waited for the day Dave would put a ring on her finger, like he promised.

It was hard to keep up with Dave's whereabouts in the 1980s. If he wasn't with Bonnie in Clearwater, he was going from one motel to another, setting up drugs or gun deals, or was sleeping at JoAnne's small apartment, turning up when he felt like it.

Riley picked up his heroin knowledge on missions in Southeast Asia during the Vietnam War era. By 1971, the greatest threat to the U.S. military in Vietnam was not Communism, but heroin. GI's lined up at ramshackle cigarette stands by the dozen to score a hit. Heroin could be bought for a few dollars from local children down Saigon's back alleys and on jungle roads by US soldiers via characters like Riley.

As the conflicts in Asia settled, Dave's usefulness to the CIA faded. Riley put his drug and gun knowledge to use and set up a crack house on Buffalo Street, along with a weapon's business on Cleveland Street in Clearwater. Fearing he might tell some reporter about the prisoner release program, the Agency continued to protect him.

Within the vicinity of his Buffalo Street business in the 80s, Riley developed a close friendship with Bruce Tatz, owner of the Tatz Pharmacy in Tampa. Dave would hang out at Tatz' drugstore two or three times a week for hours at a stretch. Riley also did the same at Ledner's Pharmacy on Hillsborough Avenue. Tatz never believed Dave to be the type to deal in drugs and claimed all the drugs, such as the pain killer Dilaudid, he sold to Dave were for his medical problems.

Through their years of conversations, Bruce mentioned how disappointed Riley was over the *Bay of Pigs* fiasco. Dave was upset that President Kennedy backed out hours after the incident started. He believed the invading *2506 Brigade* members, the Cubans trained in the Everglades to retake their homeland in the early 1960s, would have been victorious in merely three additional hours. The defeat broke the good relations between the Kennedy brothers and the CIA. Budgets were cut drastically and President Kennedy declared there would be no more assassination attempts on Castro stopping of CIA funds for people like him.

Tatz lost his drug store to bankruptcy before gaining employment at a hospital pharmacy in Tampa. Bruce put those times far behind him and eventually became one of a few directors of the Hillsborough County Pharmacy Association. Like Tatz' business, Ledner's Pharmacy on Hillsborough Avenue also fell into bankruptcy.

Riley didn't like the competition and knew how to get rid of it. One day, he asked JoAnne to drive him over to Buffalo Street. He told her "Watch that house across the street. In five minutes there will be a massive fire." In exactly five minutes, at 8AM, JoAnne heard a large explosion and saw the two-story wooden house instantly engulfed in flames. It was Dave getting rid of another gang's crack house. JoAnne got the clear message, stay in line or something like that might happen to you.

By the time Dave hit his mid-thirties his thirst for expensive bourbon and beer was getting out of control. He did though make a few sporadic attempts to deal with his problem. Dave and Dennis

Ward first met at an Alcoholics Anonymous meeting. Dennis was also the husband of JoAnne's landlady, Ellen Ward.

Dennis Ward, a Notary Public allowed to marry couples in the State of Florida, united Bonnie Dell and David Thomas Riley in marriage in the living room of his and Ellen's comfortable house in February of 1988. Finishing the short ceremony, Dennis faced Dave and said,

"You may place the ring on Bonnie's finger."

Dave had been drinking cans of beer and brought some along to the service. He pulled the ring off the top of an unopened can, took Bonnie's hand and placed the tin loop on her finger.

"Hey, it looks great!" he laughed.

Bonnie smiled at her new husband while Ellen, Dennis and JoAnne looked at one another with barely hidden disdain. They felt sorry for Bonnie. She went through a lot with Dave and it hadn't been all that long since Dave had fired a revolver at her with the bullet just slipping past her head and making a hole in the wall of Jo's apartment.

At night, Dave and Bonnie had loud fights which Ellen Ward couldn't miss hearing from her kitchen window.

Bonnie told Ellen several times,

"He's going to kill me, I know he is."

Dave slumped on the sofa after Dennis finished the wedding ceremony and took a hefty slug from the can of beer he had snapped open. Bonnie sat on his lap with a grin on her face.

"I can't believe we're married!"

"Hey, don't say I never buy you anything," joked Riley, holding up her hand and eyeing the piece of aluminum on her wedding finger.

"It don't matter to me," Bonnie shrugged. "You're my husband. That's all I care about."

"Good girl," Dave replied, patting her thigh.

Instead of embarking on a honeymoon, Dave gave his wife a hit of heroin on her wedding night. While she lay in a stupor in a cheap motel room Dave watched boxing on TV, swigging from a bottle of his favorite bourbon.

In early December, 1989, Dave was on the phone to JoAnne in a real panic. "Bonnie's overdosed! Come round quick!"

"But I won't know what to do, David!" Jo said.

"Just come round! Quickly!"

"OK, calm down."

Dave and Bonnie were staying in a motel nearby. When JoAnne turned up, she found Dave in the bedroom, pacing up and down on the stained carpet. There was no sign of Bonnie.

"Where is she?" asked JoAnne.

Dave didn't speak, only moved his head in the direction of another door. Jo walked towards it and pushed the door open a crack. She could see an arm, laced with track marks, hanging over the side of the bath tub. When she took a few steps inside she found Bonnie naked and neck deep in murky water. Jo put her hand out and touched Bonnie's skin. She was stone cold.

"Oh my God!" Jo ran for the phone, to call an ambulance. Dave stood in her way, his arms blocking her, his face angry.

"No! The cops might ask questions," he said.

"Well I don't know what to do!" JoAnne cried.

"We gotta think of something fast. I'm not getting the cops involved and that's that!"

"What if she dies?" JoAnne asked.

"That's her stupid fault. I'm not going back inside," Dave said. "But you can't just leave her."

"I didn't force her to pump that junk in her veins," Riley interrupted and took a swig from the bottle of booze he was clutching.

Fortunately Bonnie's eyes flickered open and she began to move. Riley and Jo pulled her out of the bath, placed her on the bed and covered her with a blanket while she made groaning sounds. Dribbles of saliva and vomit leaked from the corners of her mouth and slid over her cheeks.

Dave pulled a face as he watched his wife. "Jeez, what a fucking mess."

"Just keep an eye on her," said JoAnne.

"Sure," shrugged Dave, clicked the TV on and slumped in a fraying upholstered chair. Jo waited a few more minutes. Once Bonnie had come around properly, she was relieved to get out of there.

A fortnight later, on December 15, 1989, Bonnie overdosed again on the drugs Dave gave her, at the very same motel he had sex with Cindy and Amanda, but this time she'd taken way too much heroin. Dave looked on while Bonnie drew her last breath and lay there as white as the sheets she had died on. Then he walked out. The maid's screams echoed down the motel corridor when she found Bonnie with a tourniquet wound tight around her upper arm and a needle still sticking out of a vein.

Dave went back to Jo's place at Ellicott Street that night. He was quiet. Didn't say a word and went to sleep on the couch in his clothes, as he often did.

"What's wrong?" Jo asked.

Dave didn't answer her question. He simply turned his back to her and a few minutes later he began to snore.

The next day, two Tampa Police detectives stopped at the apartment to ask questions about the death and suddenly Riley clutched at his stomach and slumped on the sofa. Jo was shocked by his strange behavior.

"Officer, don't come too close," Dave wheezed. "I've got a contagious disease and I'm worried you might get it."

The two officers looked alarmed and took a few paces backwards as Dave coughed and gagged. He never had a particularly healthy glow anyhow, so this just added to the whole effect.

"The doctors don't know how long I have left." gurgled Dave. "Could be any time."

"OK, Mr. Riley, we better leave you to it," said the younger cop, his hand covering his mouth.

"We'll wrap this up now," said the other cop, heading quickly for the door, his partner inches behind. "I guess Mrs. Riley's death was an accident."

"Sure, and it won't be long before I'll be joining my wife," spluttered Dave, lying back on the sofa. "Up there with the angels."

Dave looked at the crack on the ceiling like the Archangel Gabriel himself had appeared through the clouds. The cops almost ran to their car and drove off.

There was no inquest into the cause of Bonnie's death and no one came to question Dave again. Her mother had her buried in a quiet ceremony with just a few relatives present and Bonnie's kids were looked after by their grandmother. Jo, Ellen and Dennis knew what brought about the 36-year old woman's death. They didn't need an inquest to tell them that.

Riley didn't go to her funeral to say goodbye. He was either unconcerned by his wife's death or too worried about God's judgement to show his face in a cemetery. He got Jo to drive him to St. Joseph's Roman Catholic Church on Cherry Street in Tampa to take Communion.

While she watched him disappear into the front of the building, Jo looked on in dismay. Being a believer herself, she thought his actions were an affront to the church, so she waited outside in her car. It is not known how many deaths Dave was guilty of causing during his criminal career, but he was brought up Catholic and had a fear of God and Hell instilled in him.

Dennis Ward died of cancer in 1988, at age 60, and his wife realized soon after that his cremation certificate was missing. Ellen was devastated enough over her husband's death so she made her way over to confront Dave at Jo's place, situated on the grounds of her own much bigger house. He was drinking bourbon in front of the TV while Jo was at work at the retirement center.

"Hey Ellen. How you doin'?" he said, bleary-eyed and unshaven. The curtains were closed and Dave looked like he could do with a shower and shave. The air smelled stale.

"Where is it?" Ellen demanded.

"Huh?"

"Dennis's cremation certificate. You took it," she said.

Dave laughed. "C'mon, what would I want with that?"

"False identification purposes, that's what."

A short lady of mixed race and in her late thirties, Ellen wasn't the type to suffer fools. She was getting heartily sick of Dave Riley and couldn't be bothered to get into a discussion with him so she searched the apartment. Sure enough, she found Dennis's missing certificate. Dave was comatose on the sofa by the time Ellen stormed out with it clutched in her hand.

Dave's drinking was getting worse. Every night he could be found staggering about outside onto the street with pistols for both hands.

It was almost 11PM on a Friday and he was in top form again, wandering about in his jogging pants and open bath robe. He had a pistol in each hand and waved them above his head.

"No one messes with Dave Riley!" he shouted. "I'm a top secret agent! The Feds are in my back pocket. I'm their number one main man and don't anyone fuckin' forget it!"

Then a couple of shots rang out. "Bang bang!"

Dave shouted manically. He took the bourbon from his robe pocket and swigged the amber liquid until it ran over his stubble and down the front of his bare chest.

A car drove past and edged into a neighbor's driveway. Dave suddenly sprinted toward the vehicle, his weapons waving high in the night air.

"Hey you! You over there! Wanna see what I got?!"

He pointed a pistol at the car window.

"See! Look! I killed every one of those commie bastards single-handed! Pow! No one fucking messes with Dave T. Riley, number one American secret agent!" Dave roared with laughter.

The neighbor sprang from his car and, head down, ran into his house, bolting the door behind him.

"Fuck you!" ranted Dave while he marched up and down the street, face turned up to the skies, weapons flailing.

"Fuck you all! Each and every one of you! I work for the President! You're not good enough to shine my shoes!"

Ellen watched Riley's antics out of her kitchen window. He was barefoot and so drunk he hadn't noticed that he had stepped on broken glass when he dropped his bottle of bourbon on the ground. She could see the shards glistening in the street lights and the blood oozing between Dave's toes. She called the police, as she had done many times before.

When they turned up and saw that it was Riley being a public nuisance, they didn't do a thing. They just drove off, leaving Ellen standing outside her front door watching Dave mumbling to himself.

"Dumb ass cops got nothin' on me. I'm a top secret agent. They know who I am. Everyone knows David Thomas Riley. I fought the commie's single-handed."

Dave also had alcohol induced hallucinations that made him frequently bang on Ellen's windows at night, yelling there was a stranger prowling about. He blocked the apartment toilet while hiding packages of crack cocaine in the tank. When Ellen hired a plumber to mend it, she saw hypodermic needles strewn across the floor.

In early 1990, she erected a big fence across the middle of her property, in between her house and JoAnne's garage apartment, trying to keep him away. It didn't make any difference. Dave continued to parade drunkenly around the place, weapons hoisted, crowing about his time as a top secret agent to anyone in the vicinity. The neighbors bolted themselves in their houses when Dave was on the prowl.

Gerald Jensen, Ellen's new boyfriend and their next door neighbor, Jake Harris, both Vietnam veterans, said that while they were aware Dave was a braggart, they agreed that his Vietnam stories were true as Dave knew secret information only someone doing undercover CIA work would know. Both men concluded Riley simply knew too much to not have been involved with the now defunct Air America, the CIA's own air force in Southeast Asia during the Vietnam War.

One late winter morning, Ellen Ward headed out to buy some groceries at the store and when she got to her car, parked in front of her house, all four tires were slashed. She marched to Jo's apartment and barged into the living room where Riley was sprawled on the sofa in the usual jogging pants and a t-shirt.

"Hey, Ellen. What's happenin?" he slurred.

"You're getting off my property now, that's what's happening!" she bellowed, pointing at the door.

Dave smirked. "Yeah, right…want a slug?" He waved a bottle of bourbon at her.

"Why did you slash my tires?" Ellen snapped.

Dave threw her a hurt look and put his hand on his chest. "Me? What tires? I didn't do nothing."

Ellen stormed up to him and screamed at the top of her voice, "Get off my property!" She then pushed the front door open and waited for Dave to leave. He simply got up off the sofa and slunk out the door.

"No need to get so upset, lady," he said as he sauntered away. "I know where I'm not wanted."

JoAnne left a few days later too, for a new apartment she had found on nearby Harer Street. Ellen didn't mean for JoAnne to leave. She liked her, but she had other ideas about why Dave went to Harer Street with her.

"Jo was very frightened of Dave. She would have been too

afraid to have told him not to come with her," said Ellen.

In May 1991, Riley stood in the living room doorway of Jo's new place one morning and looked at her while she sat on the sofa. She was in her work uniform and had kicked off her shoes.

"Would you come for a drive with me?" Dave said.

"I'm tired. I've just finished a long shift," JoAnne replied, trying to concentrate on the TV game show she was watching and hoping he would go away.

"Please," he said. "Now."

"Why?"

"I have something I want to tell you," answered Dave.

"Tell me here," she said. Dave threw Jo an annoyed look and she sighed and put her shoes back on.

"OK, OK," she relented.

It was hot and sunny and there was a group of kids riding bikes and heading in the direction of Gidden's Park, which was where Dave was encouraging her to drive to.

"Why are we going to the park?" she asked a dishevelled-looking Dave. He seemed to be in an agitated state, which made Jo nervous. She parked the car and they walked towards the gate of the park. Jo noticed the smell of stale booze wafting in the slight breeze as they went.

"Sit," he said abruptly, pointing at a picnic bench in the middle of a grassy area. The place was empty, apart from a group of children on swings in the distance. Jo took a seat and felt her unease growing as Dave simply stared at her, chewing on the inside of his lip. The silence between them carried on for a few moments, until Dave eventually spoke.

"I've been had," he announced.

JoAnne knew immediately what he meant but wanted him to be clearer. "What?"

"There will never be any money, Jo. I've been had."

The truth hit JoAnne like a stack of concrete blocks. Snapshots of the last thirteen years pumped through her brain. She could hear Dave's mantra, "You're a patriot like me. You'll get your money back, and then some!"

All the hope that had kept her motivated for so long disappeared. The President didn't know a thing about her dutiful service to America. Riley had spent every dime.

Dave tapped her hand and gave her his most earnest expression. "Hey, did you hear me?"

JoAnne sprang up off the bench and ran towards her parked car with Dave close on her heels.

"Where you going?" he shouted.

The two got back into the car and rode in silence until they arrived back at Jo's apartment. Jo turned off the ignition and turned to Dave still sitting in the car.

"Why didn't you do this thing to your own mother and not me? Why?"

Dave just shrugged. He didn't answer her that day, nor did he ever offer her an explanation.

For a while, Dave remained at the Harer Street apartment disappearing for weeks at a time. Then one day he left without saying goodbye and never came back. For JoAnne, it was like being let out of prison. She felt she was finally free.

Sometime after his departure, he unsuccessfully tried to cash a check from her account. It was the last anyone heard from him until an incident nearly 20 years after his disappearence.

In February 2011, JoAnne drove to her local shopping center, needing to stock up on groceries. It was a warm winter afternoon, but there was nothing out of the ordinary about it. After paying for her bill, she walked outside and headed toward her vehicle parked in the lot. She got into the driver's seat, closed the door and was about to put the key in the ignition when she was startled by a crazed banging on the window. She looked up to see a guy whacking the flats of both hands on the glass while shouting words she couldn't make out. He didn't appear angry, only desperate to tell her something.

Jo felt her heart pound as she clicked the engine into gear. She peered closer as the man's white hair hanging over his ears and forehead, flailing out in the light breeze, giving him an almost insane appearance. She looked at his plaid shirt, baggy brown trousers, jacket and the small cowboy hat perched on his head.

She knew exactly who it was. It was Dave Riley, only in a weird disguise and his face was smudged in women's make-up. His cheeks were daubed with red and his lips painted the same color. Bizarrely, despite her fear, Jo noticed that he actually looked a lot healthier than he did in his drinking and drug dealing days and had gained a few pounds.

"Leave me alone, Dave!" Jo screamed.

In a panic to get away, she revved the engine of her car and smashed into the vehicle next to hers in the parking lot. The commotion brought the owner of the other car running, shouting at JoAnne who had stopped driving away by now.

Minutes later, the police turned up to speak to both car owners. When Jo glanced around her, Dave was gone. As she gave her address to the cops, in relation to the fender bender, the awful truth sunk in. Dave was not dead like some people had been reassuring her throuhgout the years disappearance.

Oddly, under such alarming circumstances, she observed that Dave had been wearing smart shoes that day and not his signature cowboy boots that she always hated.

"I know for sure it was Dave," JoAnne informed her son a few days later. "I've written to the FBI in Washington, telling them I can't rest until I know his whereabouts."

The FBI ignored her request for information. The ATF, having also investigated Riley's illegal firearms and drug sales, also chose not to reveal whether if Riley is dead or alive.

JoAnne lives in fear that he could return any day. Each night she checks out of her bedroom window to make sure Dave isn't in the yard, ready to break-in and asks "Is he coming back to haunt me?"

TWENTY

C HALLENGED BY EPILEPSY AND dyslexia, early life was a disappointment for David Thomas Riley. Dave grew up feeling weaker than and resentful towards of his four older sporty alpha-male brothers who made their father Patrick proud. Yearning to prove to his family he was somebody important, Dave dreamt big. A desire to be a superstar recording artist led the adolescent hoodlum into the fringes of organized crime. Ironically though, it was his failed extortion attempt at the bus station in June 1960, weeks after his 21st birthday, that landed Dave in the jail where he found his calling.

The CIA's policy of recruiting whomever it deemed suitable to carry out spying missions spawned a raft of operatives from difficult backgrounds. Recruits had to be street-smart, confident, intellegent, quick-studies, pliable, loyal, lacking in empathy, and most importantly, willing to risk their life for a chance at freedom from prison. Being all this, Dave was trained by the Feds to operate in a complex world of international crime. As the 60s turn into the mid-70s, the CIA's use for him waned. With the skills learned through his covert work, Riley was afforded an extensive career in gunrunning, drug dealing, fraud and embezzlement.

Today, Dave's mortality remains in question. Although JoAnn believes she encountered Dave in February 2011, Dave's oldest brother Patrick claimed he got a call from someone he assumed was a coroner asking him to identify David's dead body by means of a photograph. The official on the phone said Dave had passed away during a New York flu epidemic in 2005. Patrick said that the mailed photograph was indeed that of Dave, so he informed the man claiming to be an employee of the New York City coroner's office. A box of ashes was then sent to Patrick who put them in the family Miami plot.

Obviously the possibility of this style of ID occuring is quite a stretch for anyone's imagination. With Dave's many sets of finger prints, routinely taken at each arrest over the years and available DNA records there would be no need for a photo ID. The police also have Riley's DNA records. Pictures simply aren't reliable enough and are used only when there is no DNA or fingerprints.

Riley's oldest brother, Patrick, blamed other people for the bad publicity Dave received throughout the years. The family certainly had plenty of reasons to cut the cord with Dave, but they never did completely. There always remained a connection, even after the death of his most loving and supportive mother.

JoAnne Novak, now in her 90s, lived on Harer Street in Tampa, for 18 years. Then in 2009, she moved 40 miles north of the city where she currently works for a retired Air Force General. The retiree pays her a few dollars a week for doing chores and cooking. When asked for her current view of Riley she said, "I'll admit that I'd like him to suffer, like he made other people around him suffer." JoAnne never saw a penny of her money again, and having written to the FBI and CIA several times, eventually resigned herself to the fact that the government is not interested in her situation.

Since Dave set up a drugs operation from Ben's home in 1981, mother and son have regained a close relationship, with JoAnne helping him through a messy divorce in the 90s. Ben was ruined professionally by Riley, unable to gain an interview with any corporation that carries out background checks. Determined, he changed professions and is now a writer and photographer.

Jo's daughter Katherine passed away in June 2010 of the nerve disease Neurotrophy, at age 56. She died never knowing about Dave Riley's raid of her $15,000 savings account in 1979. JoAnne's late father-in-law, Kostik Novak, left the money to Katherine as a child, in a New Jersey account, under her name. As Katherine grew older, JoAnne decided to keep it to one side as savings in case her daughter needed rainy day emergency funds. JoAnne worked double shifts for four-years after Riley got into the account and stole the money. In 1990, JoAnne drove from Tampa to Milwaukee to present the $15,000 to her daughter.

JoAnne's sister Halena lives with her husband Ted Marek in Punta Gorda, Florida. About losing the money to Riley, Ted pointed out most people "wouldn't have put up with this Riley business for long, but they are extremely loyal to a fault and would sacrifice far, far more for each other than just about any other American family." Whatever happened in the past, the sisters have remained close.

Their brother, Kobe, died in March 2007, aged 72, at the Sun Valley Nursing Home in Lafayetteville, Tennessee with his daughter Amanda at his side. The head wound he received during the war impacted him badly as he ventured into old age.

Now in middle-age, or in their 70s, 80s and older, JoAnne's family is still suffering from the effects of one con artist. No matter how they get on with one another or how easily led they were, they are a family, who, prior to Riley's arrival, had the same everyday family dilemmas as everyone else, nothing more.

JoAnne's niece Amanda, now in her 50s, still has bad memories of what happened to her in that Colorado Springs motel room in the summer of 1979. Her mother Cindy carries the blame on herself for having a relationship with Dave. Mother and daughter, however, managed to come through the years as an intact family and Cindy has a small house on the property of the larger five-bedroom home Amanda shares with her husband and kids in Georgia.

JoAnne's old family friend Emily Thurston gave up on her ever seeing her lost thousands of dollars. Her long-standing friendship with JoAnne evaporated.

It is only been over the last ten years or so that JoAnne has been able to properly make up with members of her family because of everything that happened. Although she says, "All I can do now is thank God that I am alive and still have my health." She continues to carry a lot of guilt over how her loved ones were affected by her insistence Riley was telling the truth about his important secret work and her belief the government would reimburse the loans she made.

AS FOR JOEY GREEN, JUST before Hurricane Katrina hit in August 2005, he decided to retire as Assignment Editor at

CBS, following 30 years at the company. It was his last big story and asked his boss not to say he was leaving until the Katrina emergency was over. Green was responsible for communication with network Katrina reporters and stringers in the field and wanted to concentrate on his job. Green felt that if he made a big mistake on his very last story, as sometimes happens, he might wake up from periodic nightmares the rest of his life because he wouldn't be able to make amends. But, as it went, things turned out great for Green and his network got a few firsts and exclusives, so he could retire without thinking 'if only' the rest of his life. As the last story went, Katrina was tragic and memorable one.

In retirement, he began to think about Riley again. When he knew him back in Miami, they were young, but surmising a character like him probably wouldn't have changed much. He had a hunch Riley's life story was a compelling one and decided to do some research.

Joey first traced Dave's whereabouts to Miami in the 70s to Biscayne Boulevard and then to a recording studio on NE 150th Street in 2002. In the 80s, he placed him on Ellicott Street, Tampa, where Gerald Jensen, Ellen Ward's boyfriend, answered the phone. Gerald was willing to talk and glad Green had called. The Vietnam vet didn't know where Dave had gone, but told Green some interesting information. Gerald suggested that he call JoAnne Novak who was living in Springtown, Florida.

Then in 2008, Joey dug up a whole pile of articles from the *Miami Herald* morgue in the newspaper's office building where old stories are saved and documented. And there it was, in some 45 articles, Riley's one-man crime spree, the phony kidnapping and the *Black Friday Skyjacking* trial in print.

Now everything Dave ever said back when Green knew him seemed to take on new significance. He began to sift through memories and play over even the most innocuous conversations he had with Dave as though he was sitting at his desk, clicking through recorded interviews. Now, it all made sense.

If he wanted to write a book about this guy, one of the first things he had to do was to find out where he was. So Green dug deeper with requests for information from the FBI, CIA, Treasury Department, Social Security and coroners offices. But all agencies ignored the investigative journalist's requests, an indication that Riley took on another name and was not allowed to communicate with anybody from his past life.

For two years, Green appealed without success, through FOIA, the Freedom of Information Act, whereby classified material is sometimes made available. Joey Green also contacted an Air America alumni group which tries to reconnect CIA Southeast Asia war buddies. The members there immediately and enthusiastically told Green they were quite certain they'd quickly connect him to Riley, but they never followed up and all additional correspondence by Green was ignored.

Joey wondered if Dave were still alive and if he would want a story written about him. He thought back to that afternoon in the Cuban restaurant on Tamiami Trail, where he and Dave met up during the early fall of 1962 and how he was overwhelmed by Riley's stories of spying missions to Cuba and James Eaton's disappearance. Then there was their final conversation at the diner near the downtown Miami bijou in the winter of 1964.

"What do you want me to do with all this information?" Joey asked.

"I dunno—Write a book?" Dave paused. "No. You can't release this now. Too many people would be in big trouble. It'd cause an international incident with the Soviet Union if you did. Maybe in fifty years, on the 50th anniversary of the *Bay of Pigs?*

—Yes, that's it! That's when it'll all be revealed."